SECRETS OF WORLD CLASS LOVERS

EROTIC TIPS & SENSUAL STORIES FOR A LIFETIME OF SEXUAL FULFILLMENT

By Jaid Barrymore

GENERAL PUBLISHING GROUP
Los Angeles

Publisher: W. Quay Hays
Art Director: Susan Anson
Production Director: Nadeen Torio
Original illustrations by Jaid Barrymore

The author wishes to thank the beautiful and talented Marilyn Grabowski
whose inspiration and support made this book possible.

For information:
General Publishing Group, Inc.
2701 Ocean Park Boulevard, Suite 140
Santa Monica, CA 90405

Library of Congress Catalog Card Number: 95-76107
ISBN: 1-881649-55-5

Printed in the USA
10 9 8 7 6 5 4 3 2 1

General Publishing Group
Los Angeles

CONTENTS

TO DREW

An elegant combination of

Courage

Sweetness

Strength

INTRODUCTION

I am a woman who truly adores men. They thrill me, they delight me and, at times, they completely frustrate and infuriate me. And since they're also quite resourceful, they somehow manage to stimulate, captivate and enrapture me as well. Just by virtue of their being, they find the most incredible ways to make me laugh—with them and at myself. And perhaps most important, they elicit responses from me on physical, emotional, mental and spiritual levels that I would never have otherwise experienced, allowing me to continue to grow and learn. Given all that, how could I not appreciate and adore men?

I'm hardly alone in my appreciation of the opposite sex. Men and women will always be a source of endless fascination to each other, and yet how well do they really know each other? How much do they know about each other's needs and desires?

Since time began, women have always been a complete mystery to men. *What do women want?* is the question asked by every man who wants to understand a woman, and by every woman who wants to understand herself. A question so deceptively simple it would hardly seem to necessitate an entire book to find the answer.

But as long as mixed messages between men and women proliferate, relationships will only increase in complexity. Expectations, instead of being realized, become even more confusing, and answers are becoming even more elusive and obscure. Frustrating, isn't it? Well, it doesn't have to be, because I can show you how to both awaken and stimulate your erotic passion so that you and your lover will be able to experience truly great sex, as well as continue to improve your relationship, for the rest of your lives! Are you ready? Yes? Good!

Then join me on a journey for which you have been waiting all your life, a journey on which you will experience the ultimate adventure, one which has no limits, because your guides are the delightfully multi-faceted world of imagination and the endlessly fascinating realm of possibility.

A bit overwhelming, you might think? Not to worry. I will help you experience the thrill by sharing some of the most delicious secrets of not only my own personal fantasies and techniques, but also a splendidly diverse assortment of ideas and suggestions from friends, acquaintances and virtual strangers who, by the way, have thoroughly enjoyed and been totally turned on by disclosing intimate sexual details that they might never have divulged to someone they knew.

Within these pages, I've compiled the most wonderfully exciting, seductive and sensual ways in which to stimulate and ignite not only your lover but also yourself. Ways that will delight you as they open up a myriad of possibilities for you and your lover to share.

To all of you who are nodding your heads sadly or gritting your teeth in frustration as play turns into work, here—finally—is a book written especially for you! Picture it as a bridge over the troubled waters between men and women in their sincere, though often disappointing, efforts to understand each other. A bridge both sexes must cross in order to become world-class lovers.

SECRETS OF WORLD CLASS LOVERS

CHAPTER 1

WHAT WOMEN REALLY WANT

I n today's extremely autonomous world, an open appreciation of men seems decidedly unfashionable, even anachro-
nistic. So with that in mind, I feel compelled to stave off
the onslaught of male-bashing and, instead, focus on bridging
the gap between men and women. How? By explaining how
women perceive and respond to their sexuality and relationships differently than men. Let's begin by revealing what
women are really like, which is the first key to unlocking what
women really want. That's the perfect place to begin our journey to becoming a truly world-class lover—one who is sensual,
intuitive, responsive, sensitive and self-assured.

Romance: Women are tremendously drawn to, wooed by and
completely captivated by a romantic approach. Something
as simple as opening a car door, sending her flowers, mailing her an unexpected love note or surprising her with a
favorite perfume is considered by women to be very romantic. Serenading her with a love song, taking her into your
arms at unexpected moments and starting to dance while
whispering adorations in her ear will coax her into a receptive and responsive mood even if initially that's the last
thing on her mind!
   Complimenting her on how beautiful she is in the middle

of something completely unrelated will always bring a smile of surprise and pleasure to her face. Telling her you love her, even in the middle of an argument, is equally disarming. Having her car washed, doing certain chores without being asked, sneaking off with her at unexpected times and writing her love poems all go under the heading of very romantic.

Now to those men who think that being romantic is a bit too cornball and mushy—think again, because it works almost embarrassingly well! So much so that it's one of the most powerful techniques a man can implement to ignite a woman's passion.

Especially important is kissing. Women love kissing, kissing and more kissing! That doesn't mean having to kiss her until your lips collapse or Roto-Rootering™ her to death. But it's extremely important to understand that to a woman, kissing is tantamount to an art form. Women will eagerly discuss with each other exactly what constitutes a "great kisser." Included in their repertoire are the following: soft, smooth, sensuous lips that don't press too hard. Wet, gooey fish lips are extremely undesirable; women don't want to have to look for a towel. Soft suction and tender nibbling on the upper and lower lips of a woman will definitely kindle her desire.

A woman's internal needs and desires aren't that different from a man's...

A man who can enjoy the luscious taste of a woman's mouth as if it were ripe fruit is a man who is considered world-class in the kissing department. It is also important to be subtle when beginning to French kiss. Let the passion build. The goal is not to probe her esophagus in record time, but, instead, to move forward, pull back, then move forward again. This technique will make her want to taste more of your tongue, to lick it and suck on it until she curls your toes. Obviously, with all that mutual licking and sucking and nibbling, she will be completely swept away by your passion, intensity—and expertise.

Timing: Much to many men's dismay, women seem to need more aural, visual and tactile stimulation to become aroused and get "in the mood." At the beginning of a relationship, during the infatuation stage, the difference between men and women in length of arousal time seems non-existent. But, unfortunately, as the relationship progresses, external and internal problems begin to rear their ugly heads and spontaneity seems to start sneaking out the window, never to return. Instead of giving in to your frustration and annoyance, however, do whatever it takes at least to appear patient and understanding, even if it's the exact opposite of what you're really feeling. Why? Because it's crucially important to take the time to stimulate and arouse her. Women will always notice and respond to your awareness of their needs. They will then be only too happy to meet yours.

Men who are smart enough and considerate enough to take their time with a woman are always thought to be world-class lovers. Finesse during foreplay is far more important than simply being well endowed.

Another secret that women don't often reveal is that when they talk to each other about sex—which they love to do—they speak much more glowingly about how long their lovemaking lasted than whether or not their lover is terrifically endowed. It seems that size is a much more important consideration, and a source of either pride or dismay, mostly to men. It's expertise and technique that are always most important to a woman.

Communication: When a woman knows what she wants and can articulate it to a man, she is well on her way to becoming a world-class lover. When a man knows what he really wants and can articulate it to a woman, he is not only a saint but, again, joins the ranks of world-class lovers. Sexual communication is one of the most commonly shared traits among the great lovers of the world.

Women are much more into verbalizing, discussing and virtually dissecting their emotions, feelings, moods, problems, relationships, sexuality and every other aspect of their lives than men will ever be! Given that dynamic, we must work to alleviate this precarious mutual exclusivity and bridge this communication gap between men and women. So for you non-communicative men, please bear in mind that it's vitally important to resist the overwhelming urge to put tape over your lover's or spouse's mouth and instead make a sincere attempt to communicate. If you're even mildly successful, she will be ecstatic. It's also wise to refrain from appearing as though this attempt is causing you an excruciating pain in your posterior.

If this sort of dialogue is a totally new experience for you, the worst that could happen is that she will fall into your arms out of shock and gratitude, which, if you think about it, is not a bad beginning.

Fantasy: Make no mistake about it, women fantasize just as much as, if not more than, men. There are a few basic differences, though. Women's fantasies tend more toward being mentally or emotionally dominated—or the opposite extreme, being in total control. Since men's fantasies are somewhat less complex emotionally and much more graphic physically, it is wise to be somewhat selective about which fantasies you share with her—and not divulge the ones that may include her best friend, for instance. That may tend to make her feel a bit insecure, to say the least, and might not inspire her to be the enchanting temptress.

One thing that might encourage her to become the tigress you're hoping for is to take turns playing out each other's fantasies. Not only does it add spice to your sexual repertoire, but it's also an extremely interesting way to learn more about each other's unique tastes and desires. And please don't worry about running out of fantasies, because several chapters of this book are devoted to describing some of the most passionate and exciting fantasies to try for yourselves when the moment draws you into its spell.

Sexual Initiation: Since time began, women have been conditioned to believe that men are expected—or supposed—to be the sexual initiators. That's less than fair to either sex because it imposes a relentless burden upon the man to always be the sexual aggressor, even at times when he would like nothing better than to be shamelessly seduced by his lady love. It allows a woman no latitude either. Fortunately for everyone, this is a problem with a simple solution. If you want to transform your lover into a smoldering seductress, all you have to do is verbally—blatantly and very specifically— let her know that that's what you want. Contrary to what many men either have been told or have experienced, most women love being able to take the initiative; they simply need permission and encouragement from their lover.

Now, if being direct about expressing your sexual needs and desires is a bit difficult for you, there are a few creative ways to convey the message. For instance, you could enthusiastically tell her about an article or a book you read or a movie you saw in which a sexy woman seduced her pleasantly surprised and extremely willing lover, and let her know how much you'd like to experience the same scenario with her. It's hardly a subtle approach, but it definitely gets the point across, which is what you want. Or you could leave a message on the mirror in the bathroom that she could read as she's getting ready for bed, which would let her know that tonight's the night for her to ravage your body under the covers. If all else fails, send her a telegram announcing that she's been selected in a worldwide search to be the new Sheena, sexual Queen of the Jungle, and that her first royal duty is to seduce you before the day is done. If she has any sense of humor, she'll think you're adorably funny and will proceed to carry out her obligations with great enthusiasm.

Oral Sex: Both men and women need to find the comfort zone with each other to be able to express their own personal preferences—and we certainly all have them—regarding oral sex. Those of us not blessed with psychic abilities cannot read each other's minds, nor do we have a crystal ball that will give us specific details and instructions when we need them. So what we have, in terms of options, are verbal instructions (sounding even remotely like a drill sergeant is to be avoided at all costs) and physical gestures (try to be at least a bit subtle when pushing the top of her head toward your eagerly awaiting penis). If you're in the midst of having great sex—and I hope you are—remember this: The best way to receive the most amazingly incredible oral sex from a woman is to perform the equally most amazing oral sex upon her. Turnabout is always the most delightful play, and your enthusiasm will inspire her to give you an unforgettable experience. And just to make sure your experiences will continue to be unforgettable, two entire chapters of this book—one for men and one for women—are devoted not only to the pleasures but to the techniques of giving and receiving truly great, knockout oral sex!

Vulnerability: Contrary to what they may ostensibly convey, women feel a tremendous covert pressure to live up to an idealized image of perfection depicted by the media in film, television and print ads. With the steady barrage of beautiful models and actresses, women's insecurities have grown to epidemic proportions. This, in turn, engenders an onslaught of obsessions with diet, exercise, makeup, hair, clothes and virtually anything they think may improve their appearance. So when a woman receives admiration, approval and reassurance from a man, it's tantamount to her perceiving him as driving toward her in the middle of the Sahara with a truck-ful of bottled water! Giving her a look that lets her know no one can compare to her in your eyes will melt her heart, not to mention her resolve. Oh, and while she's melting, if you happen to tell her that sex with her is the best you've ever experienced—even at the risk of having your nose grow a foot or two—I can guarantee one thing: Your next experience with her will improve by leaps and bounds—she'll make sure of it.

Fun: Don't ever be afraid or pass up an opportunity to have fun. Humor is often the most powerful tool you can use to be seen as approachable, seductive and, ultimately, irre-sistible to a woman. In surveys, women consistently list a sense of humor in their top five most desirable qualities in a man. Laughter completely dispels insecurities and provides a safety as well as comfort zone, without taking away the pas-sion during a sexual encounter. It engenders sweetness and intimacy, which in turn precipitates even better sex.

Now I'm not suggesting you jump out of bed and do five minutes of stand-up in the middle of hot, steamy lovemak-ing. But being able to laugh with a woman, and making it part of your shared sexual experience, will almost guarantee your shares going through the ceiling on her personal stock exchange.

Experimentation: Most women are eager to experiment and be adventurous but may need encouragement and permis-sion from their lover. Some women, when assured that their aggressiveness is welcome, turn into tigresses to such a degree that a man is sometimes not quite sure what he's unleashed.

With most women, however, total abandon takes time, so a bit of patience is definitely recommended. A good and usually successful way to make a woman comfortable with experi-mentation is simply to tell her about a favorite fantasy, maybe the one in which a beautiful but somewhat conservative woman transforms magically into a leather-clad dominatrix who forces you to strip, handcuffs you to the bed and proceeds to have her way with you. Of course, that may not be your particular fantasy, so you should probably disclose your special favorite and ask her sweetly—while starting to kiss her passionately—if she could help you make it come true. I have a feeling that at this point, if you've been both sweet and passionate, she'll be eager to comply.

Aftermath: Never underestimate the emotional impact of the aftermath upon a woman. It's been said many times that men use love to get sex and women use sex to get love. Although it's a sweeping generalization, there is definitely some truth to the statement. Women need to feel valued, especially after sex is finished, and before exhaustion or simply sleep begins to set in and take priority. Now that is not to say they expect a huge outpouring of love and affection, flowers, candy and a string quartet. In the best of all possible worlds, she'll be just as tired as you are and not expect three hours of cuddling and conversation. But do remember this, dear ones: If you lavish her just a little by holding her and letting her know your feelings toward her have not diminished in any way, she will completely adore you and find you to be not only an incredible lover but a classy one as well.

As you can clearly see, a woman's external needs in some ways differ greatly from those of a man. Yet what's ironic is that a woman's internal needs and desires aren't that different from a man's at all. Although the external approach between men and women may differ in terms of implementation, deep down inside all of us is the same need for approval, acceptance, appreciation and, finally, love. What makes it all so interesting is the infinite variety of ways men and women are able to inspire and fascinate each other. In the chapters ahead, I will show you the exciting, stimulating, creative and provocatively sensual ways in which that can be done.

CHAPTER 2

IN THE BEGINNING IS EROTIC PASSION

The best way to unravel the mystery of what men and women really want is to begin with some basics, so let's start with one of my favorites. *Erotic passion*—two words so provocative, yet so powerful, that they elicit an immediate emotional response. They awaken the desire to be swept away, to be engulfed by feelings of total and complete ecstasy, to experience the greatest sex imaginable. And yet, as pleasurable as they are, why is it that these tantalizing emotions don't smoothly and effortlessly turn into a rewarding reality that lasts a lifetime?

A romantic celebration of sexual intimacy improves only as you and your lover begin to know and trust each other more deeply and really begin to explore each other's bodies, hearts and minds in the most intimate ways.

Depending on your mood, sex can be romantic and tender, lustful and steamy, creative and powerful, spontaneous and fun. It can even be a bit risqué, as you do marvelous things to, and with, each other. In fact, the most memorable sex can be enjoyed almost anywhere, whether you're fully clothed, semi-dressed or totally nude. Being playfully passionate in phone booths, elevators, theaters, discos, restaurants, anywhere—well, almost anywhere—allows you the fun of using calculated restraint or letting yourselves go wild. The sheer naughtiness of tasting luscious fruit in forbidden places will only heighten your pleasure. The key is to allow yourself the spontaneity of the moment and, more importantly, to allow yourself to enjoy the passion. Dr. Barbara Debetz, a highly respected and renowned psychiatrist who specializes in sex therapy, says, "It isn't really whether a particular sexual activity is normal or abnormal, it's whether the act is pleasurable and the kinkiness fits smoothly into the lives of the two lovers. That which fits is good for you."

At this point, I'm sure some of you are saying, "Oh, sure, that's all well and good when a relationship is new and exciting, but what about when monogamy starts to become that dreaded word—*monotonous?*" Don't despair, because if you and your lover are willing to take a few risks, you'll be able to infuse your relationship, on whatever level it may be, with all the stimulating magic you could possibly desire. Both of you have all the power you need to keep monogamous sex exciting and satisfying—*if* you're willing to loosen up, lose your fear and trepidation, test and tease and please each other in new ways, and give each other total permission to play.

But both of you must be willing to take that first step, which is a very *definite* commitment to each other to rid yourselves of your inhibitions, not only sexually but also in the way you communicate with each other verbally, how much you are willing to feel toward each other and what you're able to share together.

With all this in mind, please remember that it's extremely important not to impose unrealistic expectations upon yourself or your lover to change too quickly. Allow your discoveries about each other to unfold without pressuring yourselves for immediate results. It's equally important, however, to take the first steps—steps that will lead to bolder and more open sensuality for you and your lover to experience and enjoy.

Here are a few delicious suggestions to ignite erotic passion:

♥ Touch your lover in unexpected areas of his or her body when you are in public places. The element of surprise is quite a turn-on.
♥ Say sexy things you've never, ever said before. Whisper them in your lover's ear.
♥ Give your lover kisses in formerly unexplored areas of his or her body.
♥ Tell your lover something personal about yourself that you are sure he or she never knew.
♥ Ask your lover about a sexual technique he or she thinks you don't know and tell your lover how much you'd love to experience it.
♥ Ask your lover to disclose the fantasy he or she has had while masturbating, and tell your lover one of your own that you've used in the past, one that you especially like. If you've never had a sexual fantasy, make one up! Make-believe is a real part of this process.

If you find that initiating this level of communication is difficult, remember that there is always another way to approach any situation. Highlight things in this book that you find especially stimulating or appealing, and in this way you can convey delightful new aspects of yourself your lover never knew existed and will be most anxious to explore.

How exciting to learn so much more about your lover as you're drawn into his or her fantasies! How delightful to find that with each step you take, your mutual sharing becomes more open and honest! With each step, your confidence builds and more barriers begin to fall.

Ask your lover to disclose the fantasy he or she has had while masturbating...

The freer you become from sexual inhibition, the more uninhibited every other aspect of your life becomes, and that, in turn, engenders a more loving and supportive mutual trust. And this trust will be the key to unlock the door to exciting new worlds of sexual exploration that you and your lover will happily discover and share.

If you and your lover have been together for some time and have already lost most of your inhibitions, perhaps you feel you're stuck in a sexual rut. But whatever you do, don't despair! You're hardly the only ones who have experienced this all-too-common frustration of a loss of erotic passion.

The good news is that there is a sinfully delicious and very simple way out of the doldrums, which falls under the heading of kinky. Yes, kinky. Now please don't be put off and intimidated by that slightly misunderstood word. The dictionary tells us it means "clever, offbeat, unusual ways of doing something whimsical, or given to eccentric notions." Now, that's hardly cause for alarm. In fact, in my personal experiences and those of my friends and confidantes, I have found to my pleasant surprise that a kinky stroll through one's sexually creative imagination can disclose mutually stimulating, exciting and passionate new worlds.

A few tasty vignettes can turn your yawns into sighs and moans of sheer pleasure. While we're on the subject of sheer pleasure, the *sounds* of sexual ardor are almost overwhelmingly erotic. "Talking dirty" can be an incredible turn-on. This is something lovers have always shared in their private moments of seduction, passion and pleasure. *Cosmopolitan* magazine conducted a recent poll in which readers were asked to respond to the question, "If you have only one sex partner, and have been with them for quite some time, what do you do to keep sex exciting?" Of all the printed responses, 30% mentioned talking about sex, talking dirty and using a few "passionately descriptive" words at the right moment. This kind of talk is simply intimate communication between consenting lovers. If it embarrasses you, "rehearse" while you masturbate.

To me, erotic passion, in whatever way, on whatever level, is the key to you and your lover's ultimate pleasure and fulfillment. Everyone is entitled to "take a walk on the wild side" to the newest, most wonderfully rewarding heights of sexual ecstasy. Sexual fulfillment is something you truly deserve to experience.

If you're all nodding your heads in agreement and anticipation, it's a perfect time to learn all about my Eleven Erotic Commandments.

CHAPTER 3

THE ELEVEN EROTIC COMMANDMENTS

As we all know, making love is so much more than just mechanics and technique. Deeply unforgettable eroticism originates in our endlessly complex, creative minds long before it even begins to tantalize our bodies. I'm sure you will find, much to your delight, as I and many of my friends have found, that my Eleven Erotic Commandments will be the most useful travel companions as you embark on your most exciting, stimulating, erotic journey. Oh, and by the way, you may want to add a few of your own commandments to this list as your sexual repertoire only continues to increase.

Number One: Think about it. Simply begin by thinking about making love to your lover. Take your time and luxuriate in those thoughts. Slowly. Go into intimate detail inside your mind until your body, without any commands from you whatsoever, actually begins to ache for it. Think about making love wherever you are, whether it's going to or coming from work, on airplane trips, feeling the sun on your body as you're lying on the beach, at a party, wherever and whenever you can, anywhere and everywhere. You will be ever so sweetly surprised as your body begins to respond physically to your sensual mental imagery. You will begin to feel it as your face begins to flush; you will feel it as your heart begins to pound; your nipples become erect, your blood begins to race and your genitals begin to awaken. Take it as far as your imagination wants to go.

Number Two: Talk about it. The next step is to begin to talk about it. Allow yourself to express all that beautifully sensual imagery, all those lavish flights of fancy. Share with your lover and ask him or her to share with you all those hot and sultry places your creatively tantalizing fantasies have led you. Whisper those thoughts to each other as you begin to make love. Share them in the heat of passion. Don't be shy. Go into detail. Be bold. Say things you've never dared to say before.

Dr. Alex Comfort, author of *The Joy of Sex* books, noted that feedback is the key to high-quality sex. I couldn't agree more. As I said earlier, talking dirty can be an extraordinary, spontaneous turn-on to both you and your lover. Tell your lover what you like, what you want. Tell your lover how much whatever he or she is doing is driving you mad with desire. Express how excited it makes you feel. Tell her you can barely stand it because it feels so unbelievably good. Ask him to tell you how he's feeling at that exact moment. Don't be surprised if you start a tidal wave that will engulf you and virtually sweep you out into a torrent of swirling passion.

Number Three: Listen. The opposite side of the pleasure of talking about it is being able to listen to your lover and really hear what he or she is saying. Your lover's beautifully sensual or wickedly naughty words can either wash over you like a warm waterfall or plunge you into a earthquake of excitement. Or both. Keep in mind that volumes of sexual ecstasy can be communicated not just by words, but by an infinite variety of passionate sounds that can curl your toes, straighten your hair or simply drive you wild. Listen to the way your lover is breathing or sighing, whether it's as soft as a whisper or as loud as a crescendo from your favorite symphony. Remember, there are no rules for how little or how much volume is good or bad. Just let go and enjoy it.

Number Four: Be curious about it. I like this one. Do you know why? Because, in my experience, I've found that curiosity leads to delightful new avenues of creativity. Creativity in being able to realize our most exciting and maybe our most secret fantasies. I don't think any of us wants to look back and find we didn't allow ourselves to fulfill our most erotic, exciting and imaginative fantasy. Life is short, so seize the . day and make it yours. While you're at it, don't forget to seize the night and get the most extraordinary experiences from it that both you and your lover can possibly have.

Number Five: Be adventurous. All the unique, new creative ways you can explore with your lover will lead both of you to the most exhilarating new adventures you can possibly share.
    From the time we were children, we've always known that taking risks, however frightening, taking that dare, however challenging or tempting, would lead us to new heights of experience, awareness and revelation that we never knew existed. Well, it's time to leap over those barriers of inhibition, timidity, trepidation and hesitancy that have been keeping you from experiencing all the "forbidden" pleasure that you and your partner deserve. Go ahead! Take that risk!

Number Six: Laugh about it. This is one of the most important commandments and absolutely one of my favorites. I've never even come as close to reaching delicious intimacy and enjoyment with my lover as when we are able to laugh together when we're making love. It's the greatest and most wonderful fun to thoroughly enjoy each other on that most delightful and refreshing level. Almost immediately, we are both transformed into two children who are getting away with whatever our imaginations can conjure up, and having the time of our lives in doing it!

Henry Miller, one of the most gifted and one of my absolute favorite writers, wrote, in *Tropic of Capricorn*, "They say a stiff prick has no conscience, but a stiff prick that laughs, too, is phenomenal."

So share the laughter with your lover. I guarantee you, it is one of life's greatest pleasures.

Number Seven: Be spontaneous. When laughter is spontaneous, one derives from it an unexplainable sense of exhilaration. Experiencing the unexpected can be the most exciting aphrodisiac. Some of my most memorable moments with my lover have been those that have come as a complete surprise to both of us.

Wouldn't you like to share with your lover the feeling of having your heart pounding so hard that you can hear it, have your blood racing through your body so quickly that you can barely contain yourself, to look into your lover's eyes and see that your lover is experiencing exactly the same feeling and can't wait another second to completely ravish every inch of you? Need I say more?

Once you've tried it, you'll never forget the sheer, unadulterated pleasure of being spontaneous.

Be bold. Say things you've never dared to say before.

Number Eight: Keep your lover guessing. How much do I love a bit of mystery, a bit of intrigue with my lover? That tiny air of uncertainty that keeps me just slightly off balance, wary of what might happen next, is what I like to consider the spice in my scrumptious stew, the succulent tidbits that my lover and I devour with the greatest of appetites. And don't forget, appetite only increases by being stimulated.

Give your lover the gift of a certain air of mystique. It is the magnet that will draw your lover to you over and over again in the most delightfully sensuous way.

Number Nine: Be willing. By using the word *willing*, I am also encompassing the ability to be sensitive to your lover's needs, even if they don't coincide with your needs at a particularly given moment.

Very few, if any, of us are ready, willing, able and anxious to make love at any time of the day or night. Unfortunately, life and all its responsibilities become pressing priorities, and time for sexual pleasure with our lover almost disappears. External pressures seem to supersede whatever moments of intimacy we're able to have, moments that almost have to be fought for. Is it worth the seemingly endless struggle? Absolutely. Sharing a deeply sensual intimacy with your lover is one of life's greatest and most mutually rewarding pleasures. How silly to even think of denying it, not only to each other but to ourselves! Allow yourself to be giving to your lover. Try to be open to your lover's overtures, even if at that moment you're not particularly in the mood. Sometimes that moment can yield one of life's most pleasurable surprises.

Number Ten: Give permission to play. This simply means that it is important to give your lover the latitude to experiment, to try new approaches to your lovemaking, to be comfortable in being creative. Nothing is so conducive to new ideas as when those ideas are met with enthusiasm and encouragement. The added bonus to all this for you is that you get out of that same warm and toasty comfort zone you and your lover occupy when you feel the urge to be creative and go where "no man has ever gone before." It makes me rub my hands together with anticipation to think of the infinite possibilities that are out there just waiting to be explored.

Number Eleven: Communicate. Last, but hardly least, we come to the commandment that may be the most crucial of all. I can't stress enough how important it is to be able to express to your lover how you think, how you feel and what you need. Not just through words, but by actions, gestures and responses that excite and inspire your lover to be the beautifully sensuous, splendidly passionate, heart-stoppingly satisfying lover of whom you've always dreamed.

Unfortunately, communication between lovers can sometimes be the most complex, stimulating, frustrating, infuriating and exhilarating ritual that exists. These verbal gymnastics can be the most incredible, the most delicate, the most easily misconstrued, misunderstood and easily destroyed balancing act on the planet.

But don't be discouraged, because here's something that has worked wonderfully for me. What I do is tell my lover silly, sometimes humiliating, but always funny vignettes about my day. When I'm sharing these simple experiences with him, I can enjoy his laughter because I can also laugh at myself. This enhances the "comfort zone" between us wherein we don't always have to appear so cool or infallible. This also gives him permission and encouragement to do the same thing, making our conversations great fun. I urge you to try this with your lover (with humor only, no whining, please) and you will reap the same rewards. And since life is an experience that never ceases to amaze as it unfolds, you won't run out of material.

Remember, the best and most rewarding aspect of communicating with your lover is that it is truly the gift that you continue to give each other as your level of mental, emotional and sexual intimacy deepens, until it soars to the unbelievable heights you thought were possible only in your imagination. Since our imaginations have absolutely no limits—let's fly!

It's time to take a first-class journey through the chapters ahead, to discover all the exciting ways in which one can become a world-class lover. The possibilities are endless, so let's explore!

CHAPTER 4

LET THE
FANTASIES BEGIN

The power of the written word can be overwhelming. It can mesmerize you, it can bring you to laughter or tears, inspire you to passion or anger or even change your whole belief system.

With this in mind, dear reader, imagine what a potent tool you have right at your fingertips. All you have to do is pick up your pen or run to your word processor and let all your wonderful sensual flights of fancy find their creative way onto the page. I find it almost sinfully simple to imagine where all my wicked but beautiful fantasies could take my lover and me.

So sit down and let your imagination soar with mine as we spread our wings and explore new terrain. Put on some music. Classical is always good. But it can be anything. The moment will let you know exactly what to choose. Close your eyes and let the sounds wrap themselves around you. Now, just imagine that a beautiful, magical fairy has suddenly appeared before you. She is smiling and waving her magic wand. She speaks ever so softly and tells you that all you have to do is let her know where you would like to go and what you would like to do with your lover at this very moment, and she will grant your wish. The only thing you have to do is write it down.

As she waves goodbye and disappears, no more inspiration is necessary as you begin writing faster than you have ever thought possible.

Are you on a beautiful tropical beach with your lover? Are the warm sun and the soft breezes caressing your bodies? Are you both sinking in the most luxurious feather bed with your arms wrapped around each other? Are you in a cozy Swiss chalet on a soft, inviting fur rug in front of a blazing fireplace? Are you on a lavish yacht sailing in emerald waters?

The most wonderful aspect of all this is that you can be anywhere doing anything. All you have to do is write it down and give these most delightful, sexy, sensual, imaginative fantasies to your lover as a most unexpectedly welcome gift at the most unpredictable moment.

Be bold in your writing. Be ever so wickedly descriptive. Be completely and daringly explicit. You'll find that it's astonishingly adventurous, and the more you do it, the easier it becomes until you begin to derive as much pleasure in writing these lovely thoughts as your lover does in reading them. Not to mention that it's wonderful inspiration for your lover to reciprocate. How much would you like to read your lover's most intimate, innermost thoughts? That's what I thought, too! What a wonderful opportunity it is to have your lover do just that.

How much would you like to read your lover's most intimate, innermost thoughts?

Let yourselves both be carried away by the sheer passion and beauty of the unforgettable written word. Equally powerful and just as overwhelming is the subtle ability of sound to profoundly affect your being, to move you to the very core of your heart and mind. So when that seductive finger of possibility begins to beckon, how could I encourage you to do anything other than explore to your heart's content?

For some aural stimulation, I have found that a tool as simple as a cassette recorder can open up brand-new worlds of delectable potential for both you and your lover.

Pop in a tape and picture in your mind the thrilling sensations and trembling emotions you derive from your lover's caresses. Express those feelings by describing on tape the way you begin to breathe. Tell your lover how just the thought of him or her touching you is making you swoon with delight. Whisper to your lover how anxious you are, how much you can't wait to feel his or her hands, arms, lips, tongue and body begin to press against yours. Tell your lover how much this desire is washing over you in the most powerful of waves. Let your lover hear your sighs and moans of anticipation. Tell your lover how much you want to look in his eyes and how much you want to express that you can't resist him as you're so far beyond any choice, that you just luxuriate in his sight, sound, smell and taste. How much having to wait just to be with him or her is driving you absolutely crazy. Describe to your lover that you're thinking right this second about some of your most delightful, intimate moments together. Begin to describe what those moments are. Know that your lover is now thinking about it in exactly the same way. Your lover's heart will be pounding at the sound of your voice, at the prospect of having to wait to be with you.

The next step is to strategically place these dangerously potent cassettes in unexpected places for your lover to discover. Placing one in your lover's suitcase, attaché case, pocket or purse just before the next trip will always be a successful way to inspire incredible longings and desires for you while he or she is away.

If he has a cassette built into his car stereo, placing a tape on the car seat to be sure your lover can hear it on the way to work, or slipping one into his Walkman, will always ensure a multiplicity of libidinous thoughts and fantasies that the two of you create together. And, as always, I'm completely sure that a procession of strange, exciting, wonderfully naughty cassettes will somehow find their way into your life, too, in the most surprising places.

CHAPTER 5

MIXING BUSINESS WITH PLEASURE

Abeautiful, sleek, state-of-the-art office exudes an aura of ambition, power, drive and creativity. It is an atmos-phere made for mega–wheeling-and-dealing for stratospheric stakes. At the other end of the spectrum is the more mellow office of rich, dark woods, carefully selected antiques, designer tapestries and classic original works of art. Perhaps your office or that of your lover's fits into either of these categories, but most likely it's something in between.

I've always thought that, whatever the style or feeling it evokes, an office is hardly conducive to sensual thoughts or flights of erotic fancy. My next thought, of course, is how to go about changing that as quickly as possible. Why? Because I love the idea of converting uncharted, "virgin territory" into my own personal sexual domain.

I once decided to meet my lover for lunch, so I called him at the office and told him to wait there because we were going to have an indoor picnic. I arrived with a basket filled with wonderful, mouth-watering delicacies and a tablecloth which I spread out on the carpet.

With a smile, I beckoned him to join me and proceeded to feed him bite-sized pieces of fruit and cheese and scrumptious little sandwiches that I made just for this occasion. Then he began feeding me, which led to us nibbling on each other, which naturally escalated into a most delightful and delicious lovemaking session. Even though I had made sure to lock the office door, the sexual tension and electricity between us was heightened by the possibility that one of my lover's colleagues might try to barge in the office, or even overhear us as we were indulging in our steamy "picnic."

The time passed much too quickly and as lunchtime drew to a close, I gathered up my picnic basket and left surreptitiously, wanting to maintain the almost clandestine feeling of our naughty tryst.

Going down the elevator, I smiled as I thought about how much my lover's office had been infused with and enveloped by my *presence*. His thoughts would inevitably drift to me, toward our lovemaking and the tremendous passion we inspired in each other whenever he looked around the room.

Oh, I'll admit I felt a tiny bit of guilt at being such a distraction in his otherwise high-powered, disciplined, structured day. But then I should also admit that my guilt was practically microscopic compared to the wicked glee I felt in knowing that my essence was branded indelibly upon every inch of his so very corporate space.

Now, let me share with you my friend Stephanie's fantastically creative use of *her* corporate space:

...the sexual tension and electricity between us was heightened by the possibility that one of my lover's colleagues might try to barge in the office...

STEPHANIE
I had been working on my career so intently that I never really thought of my new office as a place for anything but hard work and commitment, and certainly

not as a place for a sexual liaison. But when Playboy *had a pictorial on the sexy editor of* Playgirl, *it caught my eye and shifted my mental gears a bit.*

My boyfriend John is a set builder for movies and magazines, which is how I met him. In that job, he doesn't have the need for an office intended to impress other business types. While he goes to work in his sexy Levi's and T-shirt, I go in my best dressed-for-success suit. Pantyhose are the efficient option to silk stockings and garter belts. However, the effect of seeing Nancy, the Playgirl *editor, posing in her office in black stockings and sexy lingerie was strangely provocative to me. My mind was racing and my heart pounding with the idea of a romantic office rendezvous with John. I adjusted my recently purchased garter belt, straightened my seams and tottered around in my Chanel slingbacks, trying to keep my mind on business.*

I set it up for John to pick me up late at my office, begging a long day and a car being serviced. I buzzed him through the office door and then sat on the edge of my desk, hitching my skirt up to show lots of leg. As he walked in, I looked at him with what I hoped was sexy strength of purpose and said, "I want you. Now." John laughed nervously and asked me what was in the Perrier I had been drinking. I was slightly daunted, but knew I had gone too far to retreat. I took a deep breath, stood up and began unbuttoning my blouse. The appearance of a filmy, black see-through bra made my intentions see-through clear. I felt brazen. Audacious. I ran my finger over the nipples barely contained in the black chiffon, holding my hands on my breasts and looked into his eyes in an open, blatant invitation. John swallowed and blinked hard, looking toward the door. "They've all gone home," I assured him. Since I had removed my panties before John arrived, the open and revealing suit only made me feel more wanton. John quickly closed the distance between us and pressed my body into his. I hooked one leg around his hip, putting my hands to his face and pulling him close to the perfume of my breasts. The sensation of rubbing my breasts against his face, separated only by the lacy little piece of chiffon, was as intoxicating for me as it was for him. With one sweep of his arm, John cleared the desktop of my office paraphernalia. Then he leaned me backward, growling a few deliciously dirty thoughts. The coolness of the desk against my bare skin sent chills through me. It took my breath away. John's serious, single-minded purpose was exquisite. Then he smiled at me and said, "Now, who's the boss in this office?" There was no argument from me.

Thank you, Stephanie. Mixing business with pleasure has never been so rewarding.

CHAPTER 6

EXQUISITE FRUSTRATION

E xquisite frustration—sounds suspiciously like an oxy-moron, you might say. Well, it is and it isn't would be my response. But before I sound completely contra-dictory, please allow me to explain.

It all begins with two words that invoke delicious and excit-ing memories in all of us. How wonderful it is to recall the heart-stopping anticipation we shared when we plotted and planned and schemed and contrived and basically did any-thing and everything just to be able to have the opportunity, the privilege and the thrill of "making out."

Why was making out so thrilling? Well, in my experience, it was an absolute turn-on to be completely aroused and not be able to "go all the way," to totally anticipate but not be able to consummate!

Now this is still quite a wonderful arousal, so much so that sometimes I play a game with my lover in which we go out on a Fifties date. And what is a Fifties date? Well, it's really quite simple. It's a date in which your imagination plays a major role. I usually play the nice girl who isn't allowed to go all the way under any circumstances. My lover then plays the heartbreakingly sexy rebel with a cause—which is to be so irresistible that I melt like a pat of warm butter and fall completely under his spell.

My lover is so good at this game that it's almost totally unfair for me to have to struggle so hard. But then again, that's why it's fun. Sometimes we begin by going to the drive-in. On the way, he wastes no time in torturing and teasing me as he artfully slides his hand under my skirt. Knowingly, he smiles and nods his head as I squirm and shimmy on the seat under his touch. He starts to laugh as I struggle between resisting his advances and desperately wanting him to touch me everywhere.

After we arrive at the drive-in, we attempt to watch the film for about five minutes. Then he leans over and starts kissing my neck. He knows that's something I can't resist, but I try to pull away. He pulls me back and continues kissing my ears and probing inside them with his tongue. He starts kissing my face and the corners of my mouth. "Kiss me!" I'm screaming inside my mind, and he finally does, after taking his own sweet time about it.

Then he stops, looks at me and smiles. He knows his kisses drive me absolutely crazy. I try to catch my breath, but he starts kissing me again. As he slowly begins to unbutton my blouse, I tremble as his hand touches my breast. He strokes my nipples and they perk up under his caress.

I struggle between resisting his advances and desperately wanting him to touch me everywhere.

Dutifully, I grab his hand and push it away as I quickly start to button my blouse. He watches me struggle with that sexy, languid, lazy stare of his, appearing as though he is absolutely in no hurry to curtail my movements. I start to seethe with annoyance as he casually smiles and has the unmitigated gall to start watching the movie.

At that point, my options become painfully clear. Either I strangle him on the spot or somehow entice him back into ravishing me, as any red-blooded American boy should be most anxious and eager to do. Indignantly, I try to compose myself as I desperately plot my next move. Feigning indifference, which I know is crucial at this moment, I casually ask him for some popcorn. As I guide it ever so seductively to my pouty lips, a few kernels somehow fall right into the crotch of his jeans. Innocently, I attempt to retrieve them and place my hand right where I know his beautiful penis is just lying in wait for my touch.

Under the pressure of my fingers, I feel it immediately begin to harden and grow as if by magic. Now it's my turn to smile demurely as I feel it throbbing, eager to escape the confinement of its denim prison.

I take my hand away and slowly lean back, secure in the knowledge that he is once again mine—all mine. This time, of course, my blouse is ripped open, his hands swiftly moving, his mouth exploring my breasts with almost furious heat and passion.

I moan softly as the irresistible longing I have for him begins to take over and consume me. As his hand reaches up my soft, quivering thighs and inside my panties, my breathing becomes like that of a lioness. Clenching my teeth, I stifle the urge to scream as I make a most futile attempt to clamp my legs together. Waves of intensity wash over me as he expertly explores every inch of my vagina, inserting his finger inside of me and moving it so enticingly that I begin to gasp. Then he begins to stroke and tease and massage my clitoris so perfectly that I have no choice but to begin to spasm and spill my juices all over his fingers in one giant orgasmic burst. My body begins to writhe as he guides me down on the seat and smoothly slides on top of me.

Once again, I gasp as I feel his penis almost bursting out of his jeans as he presses it insistently against my wet, pulsating vagina.

Showering me with the most beautiful, passionate kisses, he grinds against me, his hips rhythmically pulsating and undulating, his body moving in ways I never dreamed were possible. The hours seem to fly, the movie is over and we literally have to force ourselves to unlock our embrace.

We straighten our clothes, smooth our hair, take a deep breath, open the completely foggy windows. Slowly, we look back at each other with a dreamy, glassy-eyed stare and try to begin breathing normally.

My lover puts the key in the ignition, starts the car and begins driving. Stopping at the red light, he turns to me and smiles conspiratorially. I return the smile with a nod, knowing exactly what he's thinking. How wonderful that unlike the Fifties, when he would be driving me home to my parents' house, we'll be going home to our house to continue this sensual odyssey.

I can't tell you how quickly we parked the car, raced into the house and fell on each other like two erupting volcanoes.

Like I said, there's nothing quite like exquisite frustration.

CHAPTER 7

CONDOM CACHET

The image of few things in our society have changed as radically or as completely as that of the condom. In days gone by, even the most zealous lovers would go through that "awkward moment" wherein a multiplicity of responses would come into play as the decision to use or not to use a condom would ultimately be made.

What I always found hilarious was the seemingly endless variety of ridiculous extremes to which both men and women would go in order to appear smooth and sophisticated as the dreaded process was taking place. But they were at least willing to go through the far from graceful contortions and didn't consider condoms a total anathema.

Unfortunately, there was also a tremendous number of boys who were adamant about not wearing a condom under any circumstances. Why? Well, in the not-too-distant past, anyone who was at all concerned with his image wouldn't be caught dead even asking that question. The consensus was that wearing a condom simply wasn't cool. And the poor, unfortunate girls who insisted upon its use, although fully aware of just how uncool it was to even ask, were most definitely never approached again.

So, crushed beneath the weight of that track record, condoms enjoyed about as much popularity as an escapee from a leper colony. Suffice it to say that nobody in their wildest dreams could possibly have imagined the attention, the importance and the completely unexpected popularity the humble condom would eventually experience.

Equally amazing is the fact that because of the enormous attention given to the necessity of practicing "safe sex," condom use has become not only acceptable but totally desirable.

But the ultimate irony is that condoms have now been elevated to the level of actually being considered "cool." So much so that trendy condom boutiques have sprung up in some of our larger cities.

Prospective buyers are now being offered condoms of every possible color and augmentation, from small animal-shaped protrusions to various and sundry bumps and humps, and for added interest as well as texture, even nipples and ribs. For the really adventurous, there's even the "Peter Meter," which is a condom with a ruler attached, the glow-in-the-dark variety (in case you need help in finding it), condoms with tiny rubber animals, hands or even breasts on the tip. And then there's my favorite, called "The Starship Enterprise," which is of course the condom that goes "where no other condom has gone before."

These helpful friends may be slick or dry, moistened or powdered, scented or flavored. And for your convenience, you can buy them individually wrapped, in packets of three, by the carton, or even by the case if your appetite is that rapacious.

I envision the next step being drive-through condom stores or, at the least, home delivery, either by themselves or together with Chinese takeout, fried chicken or a combination pizza, any of which will, in addition, completely satisfy the aftermath munchies.

Lockets with condoms inside could be given as thoughtful and romantic gifts. Clothing, purses, luggage, belts and accessories could all be designed with special compartments for easy condom access and dispensability.

Considering its potential variety, desirability and newly acquired cachet, it's no wonder the rags-to-riches rubber is fast becoming de rigueur. And not a moment too soon! The proliferation of sexually transmitted diseases has reached epidemic proportions and elevated consideration of condom use to a life-or-death decision. I doubt that its importance could reach much greater heights under any circumstances.

With all this in mind, it would seem almost superfluous even to begin stressing to you the importance of using the utmost wisdom and taking all precautions necessary. But if there is any doubt in your mind whatsoever as to the health of either your potential sex partner or yourself, however spontaneous you desperately want your lovemaking to appear, going ahead without a condom would be like playing Russian roulette with three bullets in the gun.

Now that I've beaten you over the head with information, I'd like to share with you a few suggestions to make the use of condoms a more creative and less annoying experience.

For those of you who are intimidated by or reticent about verbalizing your desire to use a condom, my first suggestion is to get the point across clearly by the use of prominent visual displays, strategically placed. For instance, ladies, if your lover comes over for dinner, serve him, along with dessert and coffee, a condom on a dessert plate. After giving him a moment to react, smile ever so sweetly and let him know what a lucky boy he is to be getting two desserts this evening instead of just one.

Another visual suggestion is to place a condom on the bathroom sink next to a brand-new toothbrush you bought just for him.

Putting a condom next to a mint on the pillow would also be a sweet and humorous way to plant the thought. A condom with you in your purse can be a godsend, especially if you and your lover are feeling spontaneous and he hasn't brought up the subject. If you don't wish to appear overly blatant, you can slip your hand, holding a condom, into his jacket or pants pocket, then casually pull it out, displaying the rubber ducky with great pleasure while complimenting him profusely on his thoughtfulness.

Another good way to let him know is to pretend you've heard a knock at the door, open it and come back a moment later completely surprised—stating that a mysterious stranger has just delivered this tiny package—and hold out your hand: containing a condom.

Now to all my wonderful male readers, please know that all the above suggestions can be just as easily implemented by you as well. And in addition, it's also extremely wise, in the interest of insuring your partner and yourself worry-free passion and romance, not to leave home without your condom companion.

And when the moment for which your latex buddy has been patiently waiting finally arrives, asking your partner ever so passionately for assistance can be extremely erotic. A very good friend disclosed that his favorite way of applying a condom is to have his girlfriend put it in her mouth and slide it onto his penis using her tongue and teeth, gently so as not to tear it or hurt him. He says it requires a bit of practice, but that part of it was also extremely erotic and he was most enthusiastic in his willingness to assist.

...serve him, along with dessert and coffee, a condom on a dessert plate.

Female condoms are also now beginning to be marketed, so that will add another dimension to your decision-making process as well as to your options. Dental dams, made out of polyurethane, are the most effective form of protection when performing oral sex on a woman. Although they will somewhat diminish the intensity of sensation, the level of protection is immeasurable, and the alternative (if you aren't 100% sure your partner is disease free) is rather grim.

One final note of caution: Be aware that condoms, like any form of contraception, are not 100% effective against either conception or the transmission of diseases and should ideally be used with another form of protection, such as a spermicide. And even then, my dear ones, I must warn you that non-latex condoms will not protect you from disease. And if that's not bad enough, I would not be able to sleep tonight if I didn't also warn you that latex condoms used with a petroleum- or mineral oil-based lubricant are rendered nearly useless in preventing transmission of diseases. But cheer up, my little plums, because polyurethane condoms can be used with any lubricant. So let's buy stock in polyurethane condoms, be fully protected and make lots of money.

The main thing to remember is not to be intimidated by or uncomfortable about using a condom, but to simply relax, enjoy and, most of all, never lose your sense of humor about the helpful little fellow. I stress this only because the assurance of smoldering safe sex so far outweighs the practically microscopic inconvenience of having to use a condom that it hardly seems to qualify as an issue. And until lovers are completely monogamous, we as a society no longer have the option of arbitrary or sporadic protection, but must ensure ourselves and our lovers of having a safe as well as pleasurable sexual encounter.

There is no mutual exclusivity between the two, but the reward of having both is the incomparable luxury of a potentially risk-free, worry-free, indescribably magical sexual experience.

CHAPTER 8

FANTASTIC
PHONE SEX

Some of the most rewarding aspects of today's sophisticated communication systems are the enormous possibilities they afford us. But the instrument to which I will always be grateful is my simple, trusty bedside telephone. Not only has it given me one of my most deliciously delectable memories, but it has also helped me to implement one of my most tantalizing fantasies. Allow me to share my experience with you and perhaps you'll be inspired to indulge yourself in something similar if you find yourself in the same circumstance.

A few months ago, my lover had to go out of town on business and, although he was going to be gone for at least a month, we had made plans for me to visit him in the next few weeks. Unfortunately, my schedule didn't permit me to leave, and we had to spend the entire time apart. At first it was totally frustrating not to be able to see him or be with him. But then he changed everything by introducing me to the most sinfully irresistible phone sex I've ever experienced.

One night he called and his tone was different, almost hypnotic. He began whispering my name three or four times very slowly, then he asked me to sit in a comfortable chair, lean way back and close my eyes. Next he asked me to feel his mouth kissing my face, my neck, all around my eyes, then his tongue flicking in and out of my ears. He asked me to feel his mouth moving onto mine, sucking my top lip, licking the corners of my mouth, sucking my bottom lip and then moving his tongue inside my mouth, finding my tongue to lick, to suck on, to explore. He whispered my name again and said, "Feel my mouth moving over your breasts, finding your nipples and sucking on them until they become so hard that I have to start nibbling on them. Feel my tongue moving down your chest, over your stomach, licking your navel, moving down your legs, kissing your thighs, your knees, your ankles, and sucking on your toes.

"Feel me moving back up your legs. Feel my mouth on the inside of your thighs. Feel my hands gently moving your legs apart so I can look at you, luxuriate in your sensuous, glistening beauty. Gently licking your beautiful, soft, wet pussy. Feel me torture and tease and nibble and lick and suck you until that moment when your orgasm washes over you in waves and engulfs you. Feel my arms holding you as your body finally begins to relax. Feel my arms around you as you start drifting slowly into sleep."

He asked me how I felt, and I could barely speak. I felt as though I were in the afterglow of one of the most beautiful sexual experiences I've ever had. An experience that he created just for me.

Needless to say, that was just the beginning of our sensuous phone sex. All I could think of was our next phone call, because then it was my turn to tell him what I would do to turn him on—and I couldn't wait!

I felt as though I were in the afterglow of one of the most beautiful sexual experiences I've ever had.

Remember, phone sex doesn't have to be long distance. It can be from your office, from a restaurant, from a pay phone, a car phone, anyplace, anywhere.

Just be creative, just be spontaneous, just be daring.

My friend Kim has also had a fantastic adventure with great phone sex:

KIM

It happens when I know Greg is on the way home, usually from the office. When the phone rings, it sends a thrill right through me. I pick up the phone and listen, trembling slightly. For a moment, there is just that sort of hollow sound, and then I hear Greg speak.

"I'm in a phone booth so near to you that I can already smell your sweet perfume," the voice says. Oh, poetic this guy is, and does it get my attention. But he usually slides from poetic to porno with something like, "I have one hand on this phone and the other hand in my pants pocket squeezing your homecoming present."

Such a dirty old man, I'm thinking, standing in a phone booth playing with his hard-on, but then I remember it's the thought of me that's giving it to him.

He goes on whispering, "Now, slowly unzip your jeans and slide your hand down into your pants and touch your clit with one finger, just one finger. Are you listening?" "Oh, yes," I reply. Let me tell you, I really am.

He continues, "When I hang up, go into the bathroom and take a quick but steamy and sexy shower. Lather every inch of your body. Slide your hands all over. Let the spray caress your breasts and tease your nipples. When you get out, cover your body with scented oil and dry off with your hand blower. No towels!"

I have to tell you I do get turned on by all this command-performance stuff. Greg's voice goes on, and I'm loving every second of it. I fantasize obeying Greg's instructions and then the rest that is to come. "When you're dry," he continues, "take two of my favorite perfumes and put them on, one above the waist and the other below. Then go into your bedroom, take one of your long silk scarves and blindfold yourself. Lie on the bed, then spread your legs out as far as you can spread them. Spread your arms out as far as you can reach. Then don't move. Don't move a muscle. Just lie there and listen for me."

There's a click and the phone goes dead. I know my lover's on the way thinking about what I'm doing to myself. And I'm thinking about what he's going to do to me—and he does!

Kim told us this particular version is only one of the many with which she and Greg tease each other. Naturally, the calls work the other way, too, with Kim calling Greg on the way home from weekend lunch with a girlfriend or shopping or whatever. She tells us she loves to be just as inventive and creative and daring as her lover. The possibilities are endless.

CHAPTER 9

KINKY QUICKIES

Would you like to know what five magical words I whisper in my lover's ear if I want him to glow like a thousand-watt bulb? I'll bet you would! The words are so easy to remember. They are simply this: "Wanna have a little quickie?" That's right, a quickie. It sounds a lot like cookie, but after the first time you ask your lover this question, he won't have any problem distinguishing between the two. And I guarantee you this: Your lover will be so delighted with your request that he'll fall all over himself in his eagerness to comply.

Why do men especially seem to respond so enthusiastically to a quickie? Well, probably for the same reason that I find it to be so spontaneously naughty and exciting.

Sex doesn't always have to be a Cecil B. DeMille production requiring a full orchestra playing behind a curtain in a room that could be on the cover of *Architectural Digest*, and catered by a five-star restaurant.

There is a lot to be said for racy and risky locations such as the entryway to your home or apartment, in the office conference room with the door locked, up against a tree in a secluded spot under the moon and stars, in the bathroom while you're racking up those frequent-flyer miles.

There is also a lot to be said for the delightfully pleasurable excitement engendered by a time constraint. How wonderful it is to be able to experience the unexpected pleasure of the unexpected sexual liaison. How delectable it is to be able to get away with a sinful tryst when there is really no time for an encounter of *any* sort.

On the subject of encounters, one of the most surprisingly enjoyable rewards of a "quickie" is the remarkable level of gratification and fulfillment for both you and your lover simply because there is so little expectation, other than momentary fun.

There are, and always will be, times when either you or your lover is tired, preoccupied, pressured or simply has other obligations. Considering our busy schedules and hectic lives, it seems as though leisurely sex is a luxury we can barely afford. But take heart, because that's when the quickie comes to our rescue, and I'll be most happy to explain exactly how.

When all odds are against you and responsibility is crushing you in a vise-grip, there's only one thing to do: Look seductively into your lover's eyes with just the tiniest smile on your face, beckon him slowly with your finger, put your arms around him and whisper ever so seductively in your lover's ear, "Wanna have a little quickie?" I guarantee you that a question so spontaneous, so irresistibly alluring, will be met with a response that gives the expression "Actions speak louder than words" a new and unforgettable meaning.

When I recall all the wonderful quickies I've had with my lover and the stack of lovely memories they have given us, I can't even imagine how sad it would

"Wanna have a little quickie?"

have been to have denied ourselves such incredible pleasure by foolishly protesting that we didn't have the time. Fortunately, we didn't make that mistake and, after having read this chapter, I'm sure you won't either.

CHAPTER 10

SEE ME, FEEL ME, TOUCH ME

Teasing and tantalizing each other visually will always yield endless erotic rewards for you and your lover. After the sweet torture of fantastic phone sex, seeing each other as quickly as possible can become absolutely essential.

And when you finally make it to your destination, whether it be home, hotel, resort or wherever you've chosen your meeting place to be, make sure it has a mirror; a deliciously voyeuristic mirror that's big enough and tall enough to accommodate your erotic curiosity. A sliding closet-door mirror is quite good, or the mirror on the bathroom door in a hotel room. A Victorian-style wardrobe mirror, the kind that can be adjusted to tilt forward or backward, is also nice. If nothing like this is available, then I suggest you waste not another second and run out and buy one immediately.

Whatever mirror you're using, stand in front of it with your lover. Look in the mirror into each other's eyes. Appreciate each other's beauty and sensuousness, then slowly, very slowly, put your arms around each other. Keep looking into the mirror and watch each other's movements. Feel the texture of each other's skin. Touch each other's clothes. Feel the different textures in the fabrics—your silk blouse, his cotton shirt. Feel the smoothness of her neck, the stubble of his beard. Take your time. Continue to watch each other in the mirror. Then begin to slowly remove each other's clothing. Take your time as you unbutton those buttons. Take off that tie, the shirt, the blouse. Let the clothes slide to the floor. Slowly, ever so slowly, pull down the zipper. Slide the skirt down over her hips. Pull his pants down over his thighs. Make total eye contact in the mirror as you take turns sliding off each other's undergarments. Touch each other's smooth, warm skin. How inviting it becomes to kiss and lick. Take turns touching and licking and sucking each other's nipples. Watch the pleasure wash across your faces as your nipples are being stimulated and caressed. Caress every inch of your lover's body with fingers and tongue. Watch how he responds to you in the mirror. Show him how much his touch turns you on and drives you crazy as he watches your reactions to his caresses. Sink slowly to your knees. Slide your head down your lover's body and begin to stroke and lick and suck his penis. Explore his genitals completely with your hands and your lips and your tongue. Look at his face as he watches you drowning him in ecstasy. Watch the moment become all that exists for him as he gives himself to you completely. Smile at him in the mirror and let him know how much pleasure it gives you to give him pleasure. Watch the desire swell within him to do exactly the same thing to you.

Let him kiss you and lick you and suck on you and taste you right in front of that mirror. Show him how it makes you feel. Show him what he does to you in the ways that only he can do. Let him watch you quiver with delight

Show him how much his touch turns you on...

as he brings you to the most beautifully intense orgasm. Let the mirror double the pleasure of both of you as it magnifies and intensifies the passionate ways in which the two of you love to make love.

How lovely to experience the sensuality of purely visual splendors with your lover. Focusing on this one sense can create a truly unique encounter. But it's been said many times, and I wholeheartedly agree, that the imagination is the greatest aphrodisiac. It's also been said that deprivation of one of the senses can only serve to heighten all of the other senses, especially those of sound and touch.

So with that in mind, I invite you and your lover to go on another exciting erotic adventure. But to go on this adventure, I want both of you to put on your blindfolds. That's right. Do you have them on and firmly in place? No cheating now! Relax and slowly get used to the feeling of them. Luxuriate in the velvety darkness. Now, let your mind's eye take over and allow yourself to see whatever it is you wish to see.

Feel the closeness of your lover's body. Listen to the sound of his breathing. Smell that warm, familiar smell coming from your lover's pores. Enjoy the scent of your lover's favorite perfume or cologne. Reach out with your hand and feel all the different textures as you explore your lover's body from head to toe. Feel your heart beating just a little more rapidly as all your other senses become more and more enhanced and the need to see your lover completely disappears and melts into this new awareness of each other. Hear your lover's breathing become more rapid and pronounced as your sense of taste comes into play and your tongue takes over the sweet, sensual, mouth-watering exploration.

Tease and tantalize your lover as she waits in pulsating expectation of where your sensual travels will take you next over her soft, silky smooth skin.

Begin to penetrate your lover with the blindfolds still on. Experience every moment, every second of how this feels to both of you. Vary the pace and intensity of your movements until you both reach orgasm. Experience the way your orgasms engulf you completely, a sensation that seems even more complete while you're both blindfolded.

Slowly remove your blindfolds and luxuriate in the aftermath of lovemaking as you once again gaze into each other's eyes.

CHAPTER 11

THE PLEASURES
OF SENSUAL GIFT GIVING

How much do you love lavishing or being lavished on by your lover? Giving gifts to or getting gifts from your lover is one of life's secret pleasures that you can share in the sweetest way.

No particular or specific occasion or even reason is necessary; the moment just has to feel right.

Try putting a present under your lover's pillow, among his towels, between his sheets or in the pocket of his favorite bathrobe. Slyly sneak a gift into one of his dresser drawers, his briefcase or even his favorite box of cereal. Find creative places that will give him the gift of laughter as well as the gift itself.

Sending your lover presents is also great fun. Avail yourself of the services of Federal Express, UPS, a bicycle messenger or simply the U.S. mail. Any of them will help ensure you the delightful element of surprise.

Now as to the gifts: Flowers, candy, jewelry and books are always beautifully thoughtful presents, but since we've mentioned the refreshing element of surprise, I suggest you be a bit more daring with gifts such as a pair of naughty novelty handcuffs or one of an infinite variety of new vibrators that have come out on the market. Sex shops provide an endless assortment of exciting toys with which you and your lover can enjoy hours of fun and pleasure. New toys are creative, stimulating, erotic and sometimes downright hilarious. If your time and budget are limited, but you want to reward your lover with something sweet and sensual, buy him his favorite skin lotion or body lotion. Neutrogena™ Body Oil, Sesame Body Oil or Tiffany™ Body Lotion can be lovingly applied by you as a prelude to an exquisite night of lovemaking.

One of my favorite gifts is devastatingly dangerous, sinfully sexy lingerie or underwear that can be modeled by you and your lover to your heart's content and fuel the most delightful fantasies. A copy of *Playboy*'s book of lingerie can provide hours of visual stimulation. And speaking of visual stimulation, I urge you not to deprive your lover or yourself of the wonderful pleasure of viewing an X-rated videotape together. You will not be able to keep your hands off each other. Or give your lover an extremely erotic poem or short story that you've composed just for him. Read it to him in your most sultry voice. Watch his reaction as your words wash over him and inflame his desire. And by the way, don't be too surprised if you don't get to finish reading your composition. I'm sure you won't mind one bit.

One of the ultimate gifts to lavish on your lover, however, is to meet him in an unexpected place in an unexpected way. For example, one of the best places I have found to give this gift is one of the most potentially annoying places in the world—the airport.

The stress and aggravation of a long business trip can sometimes be about as pleasant as having a root canal. Even the arrival can be a bummer with air traffic delays, first-time travelers blocking aisles, luggage that has somehow disappeared from the time you checked it in, long waits in the taxi line or a soggy walk in the rain to your car which you left in a packed lot miles from the terminal. All this, of course, after you've endured bumpy air, lousy food, cramped legs and the two garrulous passengers sitting next to you who have managed to get on board with no reading material and who think the neatest thing in the world is to "get to know you." Now we've all experienced many acceptable, even superior, airline flights, but you've got to admit the odds are not exactly in your favor. If you find your traveling lover arrives home cranky and tired, maybe you can surprise him next time with a personal greeting custom-tailored to tickle his fancy with the most delightful of feathers. A perfect example is my friend Sondra's amorous adventure.

SONDRA

After a long trip, Jay could barely get home before he crashed and burned. I mean he was really exhausted, typically with no interest in anything other than a hot shower, a quick dinner and jumping into bed. For sleep—that's it. After a few homecomings like that, which didn't exactly delight me, I just decided that Jay needed a more stimulating welcome home from a friendly face and even friendlier body.

When he crawled off his next airplane, he found me waiting near the exit ramp. He was surprised and pleased with my considerate gesture, but his eyebrows raised when he checked out my outfit. I decided on a pair of cherry red cowboy boots and a fur-lined black plastic raincoat. Period. Jay radared my cleavage as it peeped out of the coat lapels and immediately assumed the worst. Or maybe it was the best.

After a quick opening kiss, he threw his arms around me and murmured, "Holy Jesus, you're naked under there, aren't you?" A few of his fingers managed to make a tentative exploration in the direction of my cleavage. He was right, of course. I was wickedly naked above those

I was wickedly naked above those boots and beneath my coat.

boots and beneath my coat. Wow, did I have his full attention. It seemed that instantly, all the aggravation of the trip was dismissed.

Jay's eyes darted around the gate area to see if anyone else suspected what he knew. With the frantic little scene he was making, I felt suddenly like every pair of male eyes around me had X-ray vision. It only made me feel sexier as I nonchalantly put my hands in my pockets and eased the coat up to reveal just a bit more of my bare legs. I was aware that he was rubbing his body against my back as we waited for the luggage. He nuzzled my neck and he put his tongue against my bare upper back. The hairs on my neck were standing on end and I could feel the sexual tension coming through his skin. We were in a packed crowd of people and almost everyone else seemed too occupied with watching the luggage tumble from the conveyor to pay much attention to us. The fur lining against my backside was heaven, and I had to bite my lip to keep from moaning. When we started to walk to my car, we saw that the rain had stopped. The night was just as moist and lush as the down between my legs. Just as we were leaving the crosswalk, Jay gave me a quick, proprietary goose under my coat, and I shrieked, dropping my purse into a puddle. We grabbed each other and laughed and laughed. Let me tell you, the drive home was quite interesting, and once we got there, we barely got inside the door before—well, you know.

There was another time when Jay took the car and left it in the airport parking lot. On the night he returned, I sneaked into the back seat. He arrived and drove toward the ticket booth. As he was waiting in line to pay, I slid my high heels around both sides of his neck. It was slightly acrobatic for me, but the feeling of my stockings against his neck and chest was a quick turn-on for me and even quicker turn-on for him. We didn't even make it all the way home that night.

Jay never tires of my airport games. I do vary the coats and some are much shorter and skimpier than others. He bought me a velvet one for Christmas, and I can't wait until the next time he goes out of town.

Don't forget, this is the most fun when it works both ways.

Men can create an erotic greeting for their lovers, too. Are you up for it? Do you dare? Yes, you most certainly do. Give your lover a greeting he or she will never forget.

It's not necessary to go all the way to the airport to provide a memorable greeting. Begin by greeting your lover at the door with two glasses of perfectly chilled champagne, slinky, sexy lingerie, and beautifully scented flowers. Pull the petals from a bunch of roses and sprinkle them all over the sofa as you lead him gently toward the couch and begin to remove his clothes. Have your body covered with a coating of slippery, glistening, scented body oil and slide it seductively and suggestively all over his body as you let him know how glad you are to see him because you missed him so much.

Greet your lover this way one or two times and, believe me, you will soon have the pleasure of seeing the delight and anticipation with which he will rush home to solve the sweetly suspenseful mystery of exactly what kind of sinfully sensuous welcome he is about to experience. As I said earlier, the ultimate gift to lavish on your lover can definitely be yourself.

CHAPTER 12

MAKING MAGICAL MEMORIES

I've always believed that creating wonderful memories with your lover will keep love and passion not only alive and well, but flourishing.

One of my fondest and most special memories that I share with my own lover is the time I whisked him away for the weekend for a sweet surprise. I began by telling him he couldn't ask any questions. He simply had to pack an overnight bag and leave the rest to me. When he was ready, I guided him toward the passenger side of my car and told him to get in. Gliding into the driver's seat, I asked him to close his eyes and relax while I inserted a tape of sexy music into the tape deck. After driving about two hours or so, I pulled into the gates of a luxurious resort in the Palm Springs area. I asked him to wait in the car while I went to the office and got the keys to our own private villa. We took our bags inside, freshened up and got ready to go to dinner. We went to a lovely Mexican restaurant in the resort's beautiful courtyard and intermittently smiled and stared at each other while being enveloped by authentic mariachi music. I remember eating slowly, deliberately taking my time as I stroked every part of his body that I could reach with my bare foot under the table. By the time we left, we could hardly keep our hands off each other.

When we arrived back at our secluded villa, I went to the refrigerator, took out the bottle of champagne I had secretly ordered, got two glasses, and asked my lover to join me outside. Beckoning him over to the Jacuzzi, which was set at just the right temperature, I told him to remove all his clothes except his boxers. I then began to slowly remove all of mine except for my bra and panties. Slipping my hand into his, we slid into the warm, bubbly water. We toasted each other with the champagne and then leaned our heads back to gaze at the huge, overwhelmingly beautiful stars that seemed to hover over our heads so closely that we could almost reach out and touch them.

Smiling at my lover, I told him he wasn't allowed to touch me just yet. He was only allowed to watch as the water cascaded over him and massaged his body. Slowly, I moved over to a well-placed jet and allowed the water to tease, massage and play with me until I reached orgasm. I turned to my lover's enraptured face and knew he had taken total pleasure in watching my response to the sensual power of the jets.

Reaching behind my back, I removed my bra and then my panties, and stood up on the ledge so he could watch the water glisten and slide off my body. At that point, neither of us could wait another second, so I literally jumped over to where he was sitting, sat in his lap, straddled him and began showering him with the most passionate of kisses, and after making him wait this long to touch me, I unleashed a virtual torrent of desire as he began to kiss and lick and taste every inch of my smooth, slippery body.

By the time we left, we could hardly keep our hands off each other.

Suddenly, I felt myself being lifted out of the water and placed on the ledge of the Jacuzzi so that my beautifully giving lover could give me the best oral sex I could ever imagine and experienced yet another orgasm.

"Darling, it's my turn," I whispered in his ear, as I slid back into the water and slipped my mouth around his lovely warm, wet penis. After he reached orgasm, we held each other tightly, feeling the hot water rush over us, surrounded by the beautiful bubbles, the moon and the stars.

Whenever he and I want to invoke special memories, we think about that unforgettably sensual night that became the first of many in our magical memory book.

I doubt that you need any more persuasion to add this smoldering adventure to your own ever-growing cache of memories.

CHAPTER 13

EXPLORING THE SENSUAL PLEASURE OF EACH OTHER

The sense of smell can affect us to such a degree that it can almost sweep us away. There is nothing more deliciously sensual than the warm, familiar, unmistakable scent of my lover's body. Sometimes when he's away, I'll close my eyes and smell his T-shirt, and I can almost feel his presence. Then I'll take off my clothes, slip the T-shirt over my head and feel his arms wrapping around me, the aroma of his body washing over me.

The smell of his cologne will send me into an immediate remembrance of where we were and what delightful moment we were sharing when last I smelled it.

There are times when I'm reminded of him whether I want to be or not simply because someone walks by wearing the same cologne. That's when I smile a secret smile and think about how much I can't wait to see him and be in his arms.

There are times when I remember shoving him into the shower, especially after a rough day of work, a long trip, or a dusty, sweaty afternoon of sports or working out. With delightfully smelling gels or sensual lotions, I find myself right there in the shower with him, ready to show him what squeaky clean is all about. What could be better than to soap your hands and rub them all over his entire body, making it slippery and slick and sopping and dripping and gleaming?

Allow your hands to explore as you rub and squeeze and stroke and gently probe every inch of your lover's body. Give yourself and each other the soapy, sensuous pleasure of washing your lover's hair. Lather your lover's head. Massage it slowly before you rinse the shampoo. Trace with your fingers the path the shampoo is making down your lover's body. When you get to the genitals, wash them slowly and sensuously. Let the water rinse away the soap as your fingers continue to stroke and explore this beautifully responsive area. Slowly kneel down and let your lover feel your mouth and tongue on his genitals. What a beautifully sensual way to bring him to complete arousal.

Feel the warm, stinging jet of the shower spray splashing on your shoulders and running through your hair as your lover tingles with pleasure.

Reach for the aerosol shaving cream and smooth it all over your lover's body using great big gobs, and don't forget to rub it all over your lover's nipples.

Remember, showering together or bathing together before you make love makes both you and your lover deliciously devourable, eminently edible and most properly potent.

...the possibility of shaving his lady's silky tuft will send him running for a razor and shaving cream.

Another thing that's not only fun but also funny is when you and your lover serenade each other as you sing along with a waterproof radio in the shower. Allow your voices to alternate between sexy and silly. What a perfect place to simply laugh and play.

After you finish your bath or shower, don't reach for towels waiting on the rack. Instead, reach for your hair dryer. The warm (not hot!) blowing action won't wipe away the fragrant oils and body lotions used during your shower, and it'll leave your skin soft, warm and tingly. Explore with your lover the areas of your bodies that respond most to the soft warm air that feels like the touch of a hundred warm feathers caressing you both.

Luxuriate in the exploration of each other. Delight in the feelings it evokes. Since the beginning of time, the mere sight of a woman's body, whether suggestively dressed, scantily clad or completely nude, has been an extremely sensuous visual pleasure for a man to behold. And since the so-called sexual revolution of the 1960s, women have been much more candid about admitting that they derive an equal amount of pleasure from enjoying a man's body in exactly the same way.

The sight of a woman's pubic hair has always been a strong turn-on for a man, equaled only perhaps by the curiosity of what she might look like if she were partially or even completely shaved. The thought of that sensitive, sensual and mysterious area of a female body being rendered smooth and glistening and bare will bring out the erotic barber in many men! Although he wouldn't dream of shaving his own pubic hair, the possibility of shaving his lady's silky tuft will send him running for a razor and shaving cream.

But remember, this is a delicate area and must be handled with care. It's fun to start with a comb and scissors to trim and shape. Then I recommend that you both use her razor. His blade may be too sharp. The next is to select a shaving cream that you both enjoy and apply it slowly and thoroughly. Taking your time is part of the fun. Or if you'd rather use an electric shaver, that's also fun. Especially when you discover the similarity of the hum of an electric shaver to that of a vibrator. Just make sure you're out of the shower!

Let your imagination be your guide, and don't be afraid to express your artistic creativity. Who knows, you may be a pubic Picasso. You'll never really know until you try. You may remove all the hair you like—remember, it does grow back—or you can form a heart-shaped cutout or maybe a star shape or go wherever your imagination takes you.

When you're finished with your creation, apply a lovely, sweet-scented skin cream to the area with soft, sensitive strokes.

Wait, don't put away that razor. A man provides an equally delightful, sensual canvas for his lady to be as creative as her heart desires. And how erotic for that lady to be able to run her fingers or her tongue over her lover's smooth, hairless chest, underarms and genitals. The place where a man's legs connect with his genital area and around his testicles is a part of his body that is so sensitive and so lovely to explore when it isn't completely hidden in all that pubic hair. If you lather him lovingly with shaving cream and shave him like an experienced geisha, you may be pleasantly surprised to find him requesting this service on a regular basis.

There are many scents of shaving cream—including coconut or lime or peppermint or spice—that provide delightful, sensual experiences. Mentholated shaving cream is also one of my favorites, as it leaves an erotic reminder of a light, lingering, skin-tingling sensation both in the genital area and around the nipples.

Oh, and while we're on the subject of the pleasures of shaving cream, I want to remind you of one of the most enjoyable things I used to do when I was a child: shaving cream wars!

Jump into the shower with your lover and blast away at each other until you both dissolve into laughter. Then rub it all over each other's newly shaved bodies, rinse slowly, and then thoroughly allow yourselves to simply relax and enjoy this delightful, stimulating and sensual experience.

Are you ready for more? Have you ever wondered if blondes truly have more fun? Well, here's a perfect opportunity to find out. Why not try adding a bit of color to your lives, especially to your pubic hair. It can be one color, any color, or, if you feel creative, any combination of colors.

My friends Gina and Tony were generous enough to share their amorous adventure. You might want to try it as well:

GINA AND TONY

I shaped my own personal Valentine for Tony last February, and he couldn't believe his eyes, or his lips. I also made some hair spray out of sugar, water and oil of peppermint to keep the shape better and make it a candy Valentine. After I trimmed myself, I also tinted my pubic hair a lovely shade of Valentine red and waited for Tony to find his special present. I used a temporary hair color that's easy to wash out if he didn't like it. But he did.

I've also tried the flags of about 14 nations when I put my mind to it. My favorite is Morocco with black, yellow and red stripes. Zebra stripes are also a lot of fun. It turns me into an animal for the night.

Tony has a collection of Polaroids of my art for his most intimate gallery, and he says he can remember special moments in our love-making when he savored these creations for the first time. It's fun to be an artist when you have such an appreciative audience, and I'm dying to try out some new ideas on him. The Leaning Tower of Pisa? A fountain emerging from a blue lake? A red, white and blue flagpole? A sweet candy cane, or at least the best part of one? Maybe his-and-her hearts, but his has an arrow...

Perhaps these creations won't be found in any museum—but an art exhibit in a boudoir can be just as culturally stimulating.

CHAPTER 14

LUSCIOUS LESSONS IN LOVEMAKING, PART I

Perhaps some of the men who are reading this chapter already know how to perform the most earth-moving, mind-blowing oral sex on their lovers. Perhaps some of you know some of what there is to know about this act of giving your lover sheer, unadulterated, glorious pleasure. And perhaps some of you don't know that much about the subject at all. To all of the above, no matter in which category you happen to fall, please read on.

Now, to all the women who are reading this chapter at this very moment, I urge you to ask your lover to read this as well. I guarantee you that no matter how great oral sex is with your lover, after reading this chapter, it will only get better. So let's start at the beginning.

It is hardly a secret that a woman's vagina is the most sensitive, responsive and erogenous of all her zones. And yet how complex is this multi-faceted instrument of unlimited pleasure. Nothing beckons a man with more mysterious fascination, more elusive promise, than this secret door to the unknown. From the beginning of time, the unexplainable attraction, the magnetic pull, the sheer essence of that which is woman has drawn man irrevocably, and beyond choice, to her undeniable power.

Equally powerful are the forces that will draw him into being enfolded and embraced by the hypnotic beauty of the vagina and, at the same time, repel him from being enveloped and engulfed in its unknown labyrinths. How could this dichotomy lead to anything other than complete and endless fascination?

To be a woman is to be a most beautiful and intricate instrument upon which the most exquisite symphony can and should be played. And when playing that symphony, dear reader, use your tongue, your lips, your nose, your chin and your fingers. Don't do it too roughly. To be tender is to be tantalizing, teasing and sensual. Be creative. Varying the pressure and the rapidity of your lips and tongue on your lover's clitoris will send her to dizzying heights of sensation.

Remember to take your time. Build her to the brink of a crescendo, then ease off; then build again, and again. Do it until she is begging for release. And even then, continue to toy with her. Suck on her clitoris. Hold your tongue pressed to her magic spot. Nibble on her ever so gently and lick her until she is quivering under your touch.

Then, when you feel you've bestowed your delicious torture upon her almost beyond the point of endurance, take her clitoris in your mouth, start licking it with your tongue—don't stop—and most important, don't vary your rhythm or your stroke until your lover virtually explodes with ecstasy under your brilliantly implemented, expert touch.

And while we're on the subject of expert touch, this chapter would hardly be complete without my sharing with you the expertise of my friend Charlie:

To be tender is to be tantalizing, teasing and sensual.

CHARLIE

If I have success with women—and they have led me to believe I do—I owe much of it to a couple of wonderful nights years ago in Taiwan with a delicate, sex-crazed Eurasian girl named Randi-Ko. During those balmy, romantic and steamy nights, she taught me more than enough to provide pleasure for a lifetime.

Before Randi-Ko my idea of oral sex was sliding my tongue in through the lips of a vagina and licking up and down. Period. Randi-Ko changed that forever. There are rituals and secret symphonies that your tongue can play in combination with your nose and your mouth and your chin and your fingers. For example, Randi-Ko had me start by placing my thumbs on either side of her labia, the outer lips of her vagina. Then she had me pull the lips in opposite directions. Pull them firmly. You can let your lover know what is happening by the pressure of your touch. As your thumbs pull apart, the lips of her labia will separate and stretch, exposing a beautiful pink valley laid open to your eyes and your mouth. No matter how inviting it looks, resist the urge just to plunge in with your tongue. Begin with a light blowing of air through your lips, followed by the tip of your tongue in the lightest movement you can manage. Don't let your lover thrust her hips upward straining for stronger contact; use your hands and forearms to slow her down.

With the softest and lightest touch, slide your tongue slowly around the extreme edges of your lover's pussy. With the perfectly pink skin stretched taut by your thumbs, even the slightest touch of your lips or tongue and the warmth of your breath will bring moans of pleasure from your lover.

Now that you have begun, keep in mind the first lesson that Randi-Ko taught me: Always go slower than your lover indicates she wants you to. When she begins to beg for it, what she really is begging for is for you not to stop what you're doing. Endless near-orgasm.

And now comes the second and equally important lesson in Professor Randi-Ko's coursebook: Don't just move your tongue up and down, move it side to side, as in east and west, partner. From one corner of your lips to the other corner. When your lover is really hot, really begging in earnest, then begin to alternate this action from slow to as fast as you can. Learn to sustain the fast motion for minutes at a time. Keep your tongue flying from corner to corner. While breathing in and breathing out. Relentless. And then, when you feel your lover rising to the brink of orgasm, completely engulf her clitoris in your mouth, sucking it in the way you might suck a large, juicy grape. As you suck it in, envelop it in your lips, hold it firmly against your flying tongue. When you do this correctly, your lover will experience a feeling akin to a thousand-volt jolt. No matter how frenzied her writhing becomes, don't release the full-mouth lock and don't stop slipping your tongue back and forth, "east and west," across the top of her clitoris. When the explosion comes, just hang on for the ride.

Thank you, Charlie! As I close this chapter, I'd like to leave you with one last thought. I promise you that your lover will be so thrilled with the pleasure of your gift to her that she will be most eager to show her gratitude by giving you the same intensely passionate pleasure. Which leads us directly to Chapter 15.

LUSCIOUS LESSONS IN LOVEMAKING, PART II

Women reading this chapter should ask themselves this question: Would you like to be able to perform the most mind-blowing, earth-moving, incredibly phenomenal oral sex? You would! Then I urge you to read on. And to all the men who want, and deserve to have, this unforgettable experience, I urge you to share this chapter with your lover so that you will!

To begin with, I think most women will agree that this is one of the most powerfully effective ways to give pleasure to a man—and that in itself is a tremendous turn-on.

But since our sexual plumbing is so completely different from that of a man, our lack of firsthand knowledge can make the actual process somewhat intimidating. In fact, some women have confessed to me that they didn't really like doing it that much, but upon further discussion with them, I found it was simply a case of not being sure of themselves in terms of technique. Fortunately, my friends, that is something that is easily remedied. Technique involves infinitely more than one's mouth pumping up and down the length of a penis. It also involves an irresistible variety of kissing, licking, sucking and gentle nibbling, in addition to stroking with your hand. The combination of these gestures by a passionate, caring lover can give a man the ultimate and perhaps most intense experience in male pleasure.

And I can't imagine any woman not wanting to be the one to give her lover that pleasure. Sometimes, however, it's easier said than done. Why? Because, as I said earlier, as women, we are so anatomically as well as emotionally different that the penis holds just as much fascination for us as our vaginas do for men. There is a duality in our natures in terms of the power and mystery, the attraction and repulsion, the danger and seduction we feel as we are irrevocably drawn to all that is so opposite to ourselves, to all that is pure, unadulterated male.

So, being irrevocably drawn to my most sensuous and wonderful lover, I, of course, wanted to be "the best he ever had." And how did I accomplish this most rewarding goal? Well, it sounds almost deceptively easy, but I can absolutely guarantee that it works. One night as I was just about to perform oral sex on my lover, I began wondering if what I was doing was really what he liked best. Would he like it done differently? What was I unaware of that I could do to make the experience absolutely unforgettable?

So—I decided that I would find out right then and there. I looked deeply into my lover's eyes and whispered longingly, "Tonight, I want to thrill you like you've never been thrilled before. I want to thrill your heart, I want to thrill your soul, I want to thrill every fiber of your being. I want you to teach me how to give you the best head any woman has ever

> *I, of course, wanted to be "the best he ever had."*

given to any man. I want you to show me everything—everything you want, everything you need, every way you want to be touched, every way you want to be licked and kissed and sucked. I want to fulfill every fantasy you've ever had. I want to give it all to you right now, right this second. Teach me, show me, give me all of you."

My lover smiled and sighed with rapture as he expertly guided me toward his unique fulfillment. He showed me exactly what he liked, just the way he liked it. He loved showing me what to do with my hands and my mouth and my lips, including how hard or how softly he wanted to be touched, how fast or how slow. Needless to say, I became very good very quickly under his expert guidance, and as my level of confidence increased, so did our pleasure. So much so, that now I love giving him my special, secret smile in the most unexpected, unlikely places and watching him almost melt in anticipation of what we both know will be an utterly irresistible experience.

On that note, I think it's only appropriate to end this chapter by sharing with you the invaluable experience of my friend Linda, who seems to rival my friend Charlie in the area of expertise.

LINDA

My boyfriend Gary has taught me that he, like most men, really likes having his penis caressed in different ways, depending on what part of it is involved. Before Gary, I had no idea there were several different areas of a man's penis with different sensitivities. For those women who haven't learned this, I'll tell you what Gary told me. The end of the penis is the most sensitive and responds best to a tongue lightly licking and flicking around the tip. Then there is a ridge all around that smooth tip which has just as much sensitivity.

When I am sucking Gary's penis, I use my hands as much as my mouth, keeping my mouth and tongue concentrated around the end of his penis, especially the sensitive area right under the tip. Gary says he loves the way it feels when I keep the full length of his penis wet either with my mouth or with a good-tasting body oil with which I also coat my hands. When my hands are lubricated as well, it only increases the pleasure I give him. Gary also loves it when I slide one hand up and down, letting the ripple effect of my fingers sort of bump over the ridge of the glans, that deliciously smooth and sensitive area surrounding the tip. I can also create greater and more varied pleasure with my hands than with my mouth, and Gary definitely likes the extra pressure from the squeezing effect of both my palms and my fingers. Soft hand on his shaft, hot mouth and darting tongue on his tip. The perfect combination, according to Gary. I like to vary that perfect combination by using hot or cold water to change the temperature of my mouth and tongue, and to wash over his penis, creating the most delicious sensations.

Warm chocolate sauce, whipped cream, ice cream, honey-flavored erotic lotions or whatever my imagination can conjure up can be just as much fun, especially when I also put them all over his testicles, his perineum and his anus. When I lick them off, it drives Gary absolutely wild. He also taught me how to relax my throat so my muscles don't constrict. After a lot of practice, I was able to really relax enough to give him the "deep-throat" treatment. He was careful not to thrust too quickly or too deeply, so that I wouldn't gag and close my throat. While I'm doing it, I like holding the base of his penis with my hands, because that gives me more control of his movements. Whenever we do this, Gary totally melts and swoons.

As an extra added attraction, every so often, I straddle him and sink down onto his penis. He goes crazy trying to keep me on top of him, but I slide off again and go back to work with my hands and mouth. This combination produces an intense orgasm for my lover, especially when I prolong the process, bringing Gary up and down over and over again for as long as an hour. When I see that he is almost on the brink of orgasm, I slowly guide my well-lubricated finger into his anus and watch him shudder with pleasure as I slide it in and out, massaging him just the way he likes it. When he finally reaches orgasm, it is an explosive experience for him—and totally rewarding for me.

Thank you, Linda, for sharing your experience—and making it totally rewarding for us as well. By the way, are you sure you've never met my friend Charlie?

CHAPTER 16

FIRE
AND ICE

I don't know about you, but after having seen the extremely erotic movie *9½ Weeks*, I've never looked at an ice cube in quite the same way. A bit of ice, artfully placed, can set fire to your lovemaking in ways you never thought possible.

Start with a small bowl of ice cubes by the bed. Dip your hand in the bowl and slowly drip ice cold drops of water onto your lover's body. Nipples respond especially well to the chilly pleasure the sensation of ice can bring to a hot, hot body. Follow that with a warm, wet mouth and tongue, and your lover will be moaning with pleasure. Then put an ice cube in your mouth and glide it ever so languidly south on your lover's quivering body. When you reach his genitals, let them experience the incredible sensation of the heat of your mouth and the cold of the ice as you kiss and lick and suck.

While we're on the subject of incredible sensations, ladies, after you've given your lover the most amazing oral sex he's ever experienced and literally turned his penis into a popsicle, the next step, of course, is to climb on top of him and feel that popsicle deep inside of you—the perfect way to fully experience the sensation of fire and ice.

For yet another way to discover it, here is my friend Jan's experience:

JAN

Bobby has a lot of wonderful tricks when we play our blindfold games. One of my favorites is what he does with chips of ice cubes; not the whole ice cube, just chips that he gets by breaking a cube or that he gets directly from the crushed ice maker in our refrigerator.

Anyway, how he gets the chips isn't as important as what he does with them. What he does with them is to put them in my vagina and, on occasion, up my fanny. Bobby never tells me exactly when he's going to do any of this. He loves to blindfold me and I love the expectation and helplessness of being blindfolded, feeling his hands and mouth and tongue all over my body. Only after he has taken his own sweet time to heat me up do I feel the first sting of the cold. By this time, my body must be about 110° and the ice is a real shock. But a delicious shock.

Bobby's tongue, of course, on my clitoris, and the icy jolt of the chips inside me is something that I manage to keep distinctly apart. Distinctly delicious. Bobby tells me he loves the mixture of hot and cold when he enters me. Naturally, his penis is hot from sliding over my skin and being squeezed in my hot hands. So when he finally enters me through my icy vagina, the erotic shock of the cold is just as strong for him as it has been for me.

Sometimes he'll take one of the ice chips and press it against my anus. He does this just as I cross the edge and begin to get lost in my orgasm. Then he presses the ice chip up inside me, which gives me a double shock. Since anus and vagina are separated by only a thin membrane, Bobby can feel the chill from the ice in my fanny as he continues to make love to me— hot and cold, yin and yang.

...climb on top of him and feel that popsicle deep inside of you...

For something slightly less extreme, try the unusual pleasure of Alka Seltzer. That's right, Alka Seltzer. I first became aware that this little white tablet could provide a deliciously naughty sexual interlude courtesy of Jeff, who was kind enough to share the story of his amorous adventure. How, you ask, can this possibly be? Well, I was just as puzzled as you probably are, so here it is:

JEFF

Not that I'm a demon for hangovers, but I'm pretty well introduced to a host of headache remedies and stomach settlers, not the least of which is Alka Seltzer. One morning while eyeballing the fizz, fizz after the plop, plop, something just struck me. Anyway, the next night I was with Barbara, I had Speedy in hand and a glint in my eye. Barbara saw the glint, but didn't see Speedy.

She loves what I do to her with my tongue, and it didn't take long for her vagina to be very, very wet. As the juices came out, Speedy went in—very, very deep. As deep as my fingers could reach.

The result was only a slight variation from the famous commercial, that is, Push, Push, Fizz, Fizz. The famous headache remedy began to dissolve and fizz almost immediately, tiny bubbles popping every which way.

By now, Barbara was acutely aware that something was going on, but she didn't know what. But between the tingling action of the fizzing in her vagina and the bubbles popping out around her clitoris, plus the pleasure of my tongue, she didn't care what it was. Barbara says the feeling of the Alka Seltzer dissolving deep inside her is something like a thousand microscopic vibrators all switching on and off all at once.

Oh, one more thing. She never gets headaches during sex.

So, gentlemen, if your lover starts complaining of a headache, run right over to the medicine cabinet and bring her a tablet of Alka Seltzer. She'll find you so thoughtful, so sweet—and so erotic. If she's really got a headache, you might want to bring her two.

CHAPTER 17

HOW SWEET
IT IS

J ust thinking about the intimacy of the afterglow of orgasm brings an immediate smile to my face. How do I enjoy it? Let me count the ways. First of all, it's nice to just lie there in your lover's arms and savor the moment with soft language, kisses and caresses. Then, if either of you feels like moving, a cold glass of juice or a glass of wine can be the perfect thing to quench your thirst.

Perhaps by this time you're beginning to get the munchies. Maybe you'd like something a bit sweet—a piece of chocolate, a bite of cake with luscious whipped cream frosting, apple pie à la mode, a bit of juicy fruit. Passion fruit, mangoes or kiwi are among my favorites. Or try peeling an orange or grapefruit and feeding sections of it to your lover. Rub the juice all over his body and then seductively lick it off. A bit of honey poured on your honey's body can be an equally tasty treat. Or dip grapes in that honey and place them between your lover's toes. Mmm, delicious.

   Sharing some ice cream or sherbet is also among my special after-glow treats. Try taking a spoonful and holding it in your mouth to make your lips and tongue ice-cream cold. Now lick and nibble on your lover with that icy, creamy tongue and those chilly lips. You will definitely get your lover's attention. Try dripping an ice cream trail up and down your lover's stomach, ending with a dollop on the end of his penis or on the tip of her nipple.

For more scrumptiously naughty possibilities with ice cream, enjoy Sara's amorous adventure:

SARA

When Peter and I were embryonic lovers, I felt slightly insecure about removing my lips from his and roaming down to his nipples and eventually to that most delicate male region. I hadn't been intimate to this degree with many men in my life, and it was something that still made me kind of nervous, even though Peter made it plain to me he enjoyed this part of our lovemaking.

When I read her book, one of the suggestions Helen Gurley Brown made was to treat your lover's penis as just one ingredient in a lip-smacking dessert, sort of like the banana in a banana split. This made me laugh, but it also made me curious.

The next time Peter came home from a week in New York, I told him I read a book that recommended something he might enjoy when we made love. He grinned his "killer grin" and said if I liked it, then he would, too. I spread a towel on our sheets and helped him strip off his clothes. He lay back, arms behind his head, waiting to see what I would do. After a quick trip to the kitchen, first came the chocolate sauce, which I dribbled all over his penis. Then a squirt of whipped cream—make that several squirts. Then there was nothing else to do but eat. And I did—everything in sight. As I heard his moans of sheer pleasure, I pushed away from him for a moment, looked him in the eye and ever so slowly ran my tongue over my chocolate-soaked lips, stuck my finger back in the

> *He lay back, arms behind his head, waiting to see what I would do.*

chocolate sauce jar, covered his own luscious lips with it, and licked it off with my tongue. Of course, my tongue didn't stop there...

And by the way, if the thought of your lover's own juices doesn't excite you, chocolate foreplay makes the medicine go down beautifully.

Chocolate sauce is much more fun to lick off than to eat with a spoon. I could eat him forever, especially when I realized how turned on Peter was. He was amazed at my lack of timidity. When I looked at him, my face covered with chocolate and cream, he cracked up and pulled me up to him.

I knew sex was exciting, but I didn't know it could be so much fun. And I had no idea fun sex could be so sensual. Laughing with a lover over dessert is a great way to end your day together, and leaves a great taste in your mouth for morning. All thanks to Helen, I've been a Cosmo *girl from that first dessert on.*

Remember, sweet treats do not have to be reserved for a sensual dessert. Try some of these as an appetizer with the sweetly sexual foreplay. And if you enjoy our luscious treats to excess, you might want to get your just desserts in their low-calorie form. Whichever way you do it, bon appétit!

CHAPTER 18

LIBIDINOUS LIBRARY

O ne of the most exciting things I share with my lover when we snuggle under the covers is a good book. A good book? I can just picture your face as you're reading this paragraph, wondering if I've taken leave of my senses. Actually, what I am doing is stimulating my senses— and my lover's—by sharing with him some of the most red- hot literature that's ever been written.

Sometimes we can barely make it through the "good parts" before we practically pounce on each other like two cats on a hot tin roof. It's almost impossible to read to each other and not lose all control. And where are these "good parts" to be found? Well, I suggest you go to almost any large bookstore and pick up some of the writings of Gael Greene, Nancy Friday, Lonnie Auerbach, Xaviera Hollander, Pauline Reage, Shere Hite and Erica Jong. Or for formula pulp fiction, the likes of Jacqueline Susann, Harold Robbins, Jackie Collins, Sidney Sheldon, Judith Krantz and Jackie's sister, Joan. And no list of books peppered with skillfully written sex would be complete without Mickey Spillane; he probably invented, consciously or not, the "hot parts" concept. Thanks, Mike Hammer, for all your deadly molls wearing nothing but gooseflesh under their trench coats. The authors listed below, however, are my personal favorites, for their writing is timeless, elegant, relentlessly erotic and consistently smoldering. This is classy, sexy literature.

For your ultimate reading pleasure, I suggest you begin with D. H. Lawrence and Henry Miller, then move on to the beautifully sensual Anaïs Nin and the multi-faceted Anne Rice, who also writes under the noms de plume of Anne Rampling and A. N. Roquelaure. If you begin building your libidinous library with the marvelously written books I've mentioned below, you'll be on your way to some of the most stimulating reading that's available anywhere.

Lady Chatterley's Lover by D. H. Lawrence is probably the most read, first-time "hot" book for those who grew up looking for the "good parts." And this 1928 classic is still on the shelves of bookstores all over the world. Happily so for those of you who enjoy great literature mixed with great sex scenes. Another of this master's classics is *Women in Love*, which provides more of his ethereal yet erotic writing. This book is a fantasy flow of complicated love. You might also want to check out his beautiful poetry.

Henry Miller is undoubtedly one of the most talented writers ever to grace this genre. His collected works are among the most sensuous and erotic to be found anywhere. Among his classics are *Tropic of Capricorn* and *Tropic of Cancer*, as well as the three part series *Nexus*, *Plexus* and *Sexus*. You will receive endless inspiration from the sheer passion and beauty of Miller's work.

Also to be found among Henry Miller's published writings are his letters to his lover, Anaïs Nin, who on her own wrote some of the most beautiful and widely read erotica around. Her multi-volume journals, published collectively as *The Diaries of Anaïs Nin*, and letters, not only to Henry Miller but to other friends and lovers, reflect her eloquent gift.

Only one contemporary writer is in a class with these: the mesmerizing and hauntingly brilliant Anne Rice. Effortlessly and skillfully, she beckons her readers and draws them into her complex world, ranging from the hypnotically arcane to the explosively sensual. Able to cast a spell like no other, she thrills my heart and soul.

In reviewing her work, the *New York Times Book Review* states, "It is a pure and uncanny talent that gives voice to monsters and angels both." I strongly suggest that you reward yourself by reading her horror classics *The Vampire Lestat, The Mummy, or Ramses the Damned,* then her extraordinary erotica written under the name of Anne Rampling, *Exit to Eden,* and proceed to her three-book *Beauty* series, which she wrote as A. N. Roquelaure and includes *The Claiming of Sleeping Beauty, Beauty's Punishment* and *Beauty's Release.*

Other worthwhile erotica includes a variety of Victorian-era publications that have enjoyed a rebirth in modern editions. The best and probably the best known and most readily available in large bookstores are *The Autobiography of a Flea, The Oyster One, The Oyster Two, The Pearl, The Libertines* and *The Celebrated Mistress.* Although many of these and others first appeared in print just over 100 years ago, most are now available again, courtesy of Carroll and Graf Publishers.

I also suggest that you look for the following books at your local library or bookstore. They are sure to stimulate your libido and aid in making your relationship much deeper and more intimate:

♥ *Pleasure: Women Who Write Erotica* and *Sharing Sexual Intimacy: Erotic Interludes,* both by Lonnie Barbach, Ph.D.
♥ *Light His Fire,* by Ellen Kriedman
♥ *Tantra: The Indian Cult of Ecstasy,* by Philip Rawson
♥ *Collected Stories of Colette,* by Colette
♥ *Fear of Flying,* by Erica Jong
♥ *Delta of Venus* and *Erotic,* by Anaïs Nin
♥ *My Secret Garden,* by Nancy Friday
♥ *Blue Eyes, Black Hair* and *The Lover,* all by Marguerite Duras
♥ *Damage,* by Josephine Hart

- ♥ *The Sheltering Sky*, by Paul Bowles
- ♥ *Tom Jones*, by Henry Fielding
- ♥ *Black Spring, The Rosy Crucifiction*—actually any of Henry Miller's work
- ♥ the poetry of Arthur Rimbaud, Charles Baudelaire, Percy Bysshe Shelly, Charles Bukowski, Howard Rollins, William Blake, William Shakespeare, Dylan Thomas and Samuel Taylor Coleridge
- ♥ *The Hite Report*, by Shere Hite
- ♥ *Women and Sex in the '80s: The Cosmo Report*, by Linda Wolfe
- ♥ *Women Who Love Too Much*, by Robin Norwood
- ♥ *Goddess: Myths of the Female Divine*, by David and Page Leeming
- ♥ *Women Who Run With the Wolves*, by Clarissa Pinkola Estes
- ♥ *Hindu Goddesses: Visions of the Divine Feminine in the Hindu Religious Tradition*, by David Kinsley
- ♥ *Mythology: The Voyage of the Hero*, by David Adams Leeming
- ♥ *Memories, Dreams and Reflections*, by C. G. Jung
- ♥ *A Guided Tour of the Collected Works of C. G. Jung*, by Robert H. Hopcke

...their writing is timeless, elegant, relentlessly erotic and consistently smoldering.

I would like to end this chapter by reminding you that no libidinous library would be complete without including a wonderful array of stimulating, sexy magazines. And how, you ask, do you acquire these magazines? Very simple.

One night on the way home from a party or a dinner or whatever the evening's event, stop off at a newsstand in some part of town where nobody knows you, and proceed to buy up every sexy or smutty magazine in sight. Include in that list *Playboy, Penthouse, Hustler, Cherie, Gallery* and *Club International* and whatever else looks racy!

After arriving home, slip into something deliciously scanty, cozy up with your lover and visually savor these magazines, pausing to show and describe to your lover exactly what appeals to you and what especially turns you on in the photographs. Make the suggestion to share some of the people in these photographs with your lover in fantasy threesomes, or moresomes. Ask your lover which photographs are especially exciting to him and why.

Whatever erotic literature you share with your lover, be it books or magazines, the conversation will quickly turn into demonstration as you and your lover play out the fantasies on any and all of the stimulating and erotically charged pages.

CHAPTER 19

MOVIE MAGIC

E ver since I was a child, I absolutely loved going to the movies. I couldn't wait till the weekend because that meant Saturday afternoon I would be at my favorite movie theater watching yet another wonderful film, clutching my popcorn, my soda and red licorice.

As time went on and I became older, the movie theater itself took on a much more important role in my life. The plot, and especially the action, seemed to switch from the screen to the balcony and my current heartthrob and I took over the leading roles in our own steamy, romantic film. What luscious memories I have of my Saturday night sexual awakenings. How much I experimented, how much I learned! As I looked back on those times with the greatest fondness, I began to think, "Wait a minute. This doesn't have to be a distant memory buried in the past. I can have those same delicious moments right here, right now."

That's when moviegoing began to be an erotic adventure for both my lover and me. Now granted, some movies lend themselves a lot better to these experiments than others. I'd hardly recommend a movie like *Apocalypse Now*. However, there is a wonderful selection of hot, sizzling, smoldering films such as *The Night Porter* with Charlotte Rampling, *White Mischief, The Lover, Damage, Tie Me Up! Tie Me Down!* and so many, many more.

If you can, try to make sure both you and your lover are wearing loose, easily accessible clothing. Long coats are helpful, too. Leaving underwear at home is even more helpful.

I'm always amazed at how much better a bad movie becomes and how a mediocre movie becomes quite good when my lover and I actively participate in the erotic plotlines. We love scenes in trains passing through tunnels or other dimly lit scenes where the theater becomes especially dark. It's also helpful to time your most passionate outbursts to gun battles, dynamite blasts, aircraft launches or, last but not least, a rousing inspirational score by someone like John Williams.

Come to think of it, considering the musical score, especially "The Ride of the Valkyries" by Wagner, *Apocalypse Now* might not be such a bad choice after all.

Deborah's amorous adventure provides further inspiration:

DEBORAH

I love to get my lover excited when we're out in public watching a movie. There's something so exciting about having a perfect stranger sitting right next to you when your lover is sitting on the other side. The darkness gives me enough nerve to interpret what's happening on the screen with my guy. Remember when Jeff Daniels walked off the screen in the Woody Allen film The Purple Rose of Cairo? *Well, it's a bit like that.*

First of all, I pick a movie I've already seen on my own. I make a practice of checking out any R-rated films that have big names in them since, at least to me, the big names somehow make the whole thing sexier. Well, one that really blew my mind was Ellen Barkin and Al Pacino in Sea of Love. *When she goes off to run stark naked with that menacing, sexy music playing in the background, I knew this was the perfect film for Stan and me.*

I kind of rehearse what I'm going to do when I see it the first time, which is another turn-on, but I try to control myself. When the right moment comes up at the right time in the movie, it turns me on to watch Stan's reaction to the screen, and I use my hands and fingers to give him an extra added jolt just at the right time. I don't totally surprise him, mind you. My hand has already been caressing his leg like lots of lovers do when they watch movies.

But when Barkin makes her move on Pacino, I make my move on Stan. I more or less do it so no one else sees what's going on. And if they do notice, they don't seem to mind. The effect is just electric. Stan gasps and we pretend he's reacting to what's going on in the movie. When we're driving home after the movie, I pretend I'm Ellen Barkin and I talk sexy-sassy to him. When we get home, I pin him to the wall just like that. Sometimes, we don't even make it home. Actually, when we saw Sea of Love, *I pinned him to the wall in a gas station restroom. We filled up one tank and depleted another.*

Well, I'd say that film was more than worth the price of admission! And while we're on the subject of cinematic smoldering, another way to participate in your favorite scenes from your favorite films with your lover is by renting them and watching them at home in the privacy of your cozy living room or your inviting bedroom.

You can either watch each film you like in its entirety, or you can become really creative, if you allow yourselves the time and patience. Just make a list of your favorite sexy films, rent them at your video store and tape just the "good parts" back-to-back on the same tape. You know which ones. The ones you anxiously await while the rest of the plot seems almost like filler, until you get to those too-hot-to-handle scenes that drive you so crazy that you lick your chops wishing it were you on that screen.

I pretend I'm Ellen Barkin and I talk sexy-sassy to him.

Well, guess what. It can be. Just take the tape with those carefully selected scenes on it, put it into that trusty VCR and direct each other to sexual stardom. If you're forgetful about which scenes are worthy of your time and effort, here are a few suggestions to start you in the right direction:

- ♥ *Atlantic City* with Susan Sarandon making cinematic history with lemons and Burt Lancaster.
- ♥ *The Big Easy* with Dennis Quaid initiating Ellen Barkin to the joys of a body search.
- ♥ *Blue Velvet* with Isabella Rossellini and Dennis Hopper doing kinky things with oxygen masks.
- ♥ *Bad Influence* with Rob Lowe demonstrating his videotaping technique.
- ♥ *Body Heat* with Kathleen Turner proving that sweat is sexy.
- ♥ *The Cook, the Thief, His Wife and Her Lover* in which the latter two take an erotic tour of a restaurant ladies' room, kitchen and walk-in freezer.
- ♥ *An Officer and a Gentleman* with Richard Gere proving to Debra Winger that he was no gentleman.
- ♥ *Fatal Attraction* with Glenn Close and Michael Douglas doing everything, everywhere.
- ♥ *Dangerous Liaisons* in which John Malkovich demonstrates his bareback riding techniques.
- ♥ *Don't Look Now* with Donald Sutherland and Julie Christie. (Were they really doing it?)
- ♥ *No Way Out* with Kevin Costner and Sean Young discovering the pleasures of a limo.
- ♥ *Remembrance of Things Past* with Jeremy Irons discovering Ornella Muti's breasts with his tongue in a carriage ride.
- ♥ *Roadhouse* with Patrick Swayze doing more than just dirty dancing.
- ♥ *Sea of Love* with Al Pacino and Ellen Barkin fairly drowning in sensuality.
- ♥ *The Sailor Who Fell from Grace with the Sea* with Sarah Miles climbing the walls to get at Kris Kristofferson.

- ♥ *Tie Me Up! Tie Me Down!*, one of the most sensual kidnappings in cinematic history.
- ♥ *The Lover* (my personal favorite; never has sex been photographed so beautifully).

An added bonus to renting these tapes is that some of the rental versions of these R-rated films include sexy scenes that are often left out of the theatrical versions.

I'd also like to include in this list some sexy X-rated films. Once upon a time, the only way to see these films was to slink in and out of nasty theaters in the wrong part of town. What you mostly got was an "Oil Can Harry" villain, dressed only in black socks, surprising a naked maiden in her boudoir. Now, however, with the advent of videocassettes, you can forget those theaters full of lonely, rain-coated guys watching the screen from behind a pair of dark glasses. Now you can simply slink in and out of the adults-only section of your friendly video store and rent these X-rated flicks for viewing in the comfort and privacy of your own home.

Today's adult films even feature Technicolor with sound you can actually understand, and actors and actresses who look like they just stepped out of the pages of *Cosmo* or *Playboy*, some with fabulous bodies and really great looks. Sometimes, not always, the films even have a plot. Here are a few suggestions for your private viewing.

- ♥ *Amanda by Night*
- ♥ *Behind the Green Door*
- ♥ *Bordello*
- ♥ *Careful, He May Be Watching*
- ♥ *Deep Throat*
- ♥ *Devil and Mrs. Jones*
- ♥ *Every Woman Has a Fantasy*
- ♥ *Hot, Scalding*
- ♥ *How Do You Like It?*
- ♥ *Nothing to Hide*

- ♥ *Talk Dirty to Me*
- ♥ *The Opening of Misty Beethoven*
- ♥ *The Private Afternoons of Pamela Mann*

While you watch at home, you can copy the action or embellish the action, or make up your own action. You're the director. The action can obviously be a lot hotter than you can get away with in a movie theater, although the idea of sneaky, stealthy, surreptitious sex in a dark auditorium full of people does have a naughty appeal all its own.

CHAPTER 20

ACTION!

Now that you and your lover are getting used to the idea of watching erotic videotapes, it's time to move on to the next step. And, judging from the title of this chapter, I'm sure you already have a clue as to what that next step could possibly be.

It's time to get your creative juices flowing and pick up that video camera. James Spader and Rob Lowe are hardly the only ones who have discovered the infinite variety of sexy scenarios that can be captured on film. There is a veritable crush of prospective buyers just waiting to get their hot hands on that next piece of video equipment. All you really need to be able to orchestrate your own scintillating productions is a reasonably good video camera, a tripod stand and a minimal amount of lighting equipment, if you don't want to rely on natural lighting.

Once you're set up with the required basic equipment, you and your lover get to divide the screen credits. There's director, screenwriter, makeup artist and star performers. So be adventurous. Here is where you really get to act out all of your cinematic fantasies, realize any and all of your dreams, go anywhere your imagination will take you.

In addition to putting the camera on automatic pilot to capture the two of you vying for your own private awards, there is also another element to consider.

If you have a really understanding and curious friend who's a video camera buff, he could be the silent or not-so-silent cameraman who's privileged to capture you both in the buff. Or you can act out your own individual plotlines the next time you feel a tantalizing taped turn-on may be just the thing to inspire each other. What a lovely present: one that shows creativity and imagination to activate your lover's own creativity and imagination. I know one couple who spend a lot of time apart for business reasons. He's a photographer and she's a flight attendant. They leave taped messages for each other on their VCR if one returns home while the other is gone.

What a creative and delicious way to stimulate each other's thoughts and desires, longings and libidos.

Then again, one of the most stimulating enhancements to lovemaking of all time is, of course, music. I once read a quote that said, "If music be the food of love, play on." I couldn't agree more. From the thunderous crescendos of Tchaikovsky's "Love Theme" from *Romeo and Juliet* to Rachmaninoff's Piano Concerto No. 2 in D Minor to Richard Wagner's beautifully romantic "Liebestod" from *Tristan und Isolde*, all of these pieces have inspired my lover and me to the most passionate lovemaking we've ever experienced.

...these pieces have inspired my lover and me to the most passionate lovemaking...

Sometimes, our taste is totally different, however, and what we're in the mood for is raw, hot rock 'n' roll music videos. I'm sure you have your favorites as well, but here are a few added suggestions that have stood the test of time and are still an incredible turn-on. My first suggestion is *Wicked Game*, a video of the sensuous song by Chris Isaak. It's my all-time favorite and one of the most passionately stimulating videos I've ever had the pleasure to experience. Here are a few more:

- ♥ *Express Yourself, Vogue,* and just about anything else by Madonna.
- ♥ *Father Figure* and any of the other videos featuring beautiful models, by George Michael.
- ♥ *That's the Way Love Goes* and any of the other beautifully choreographed videos by Janet Jackson.
- ♥ *Here I Go Again* by Whitesnake, featuring the sultry Tawny Kitaen.
- ♥ *Bring Me a Higher Love* by Steve Winwood.
- ♥ *Body Like a MF* by the rap group DBG's, displaying a profusion of beautiful young girls with incredible bodies.
- ♥ *Baby Got Back* by Sir Mix-A-Lot, which focuses on voluptuous women. This video is also infused with a great deal of humor in the way it depicts men's appreciation of the female anatomy.

There are so many hot videos with both beautiful boys and girls to put you in the mood. Make a list of your own favorites and make your own stimulating videotape to be screened during an opportune moment that will extend into a night to remember.

CHAPTER 21

DRIVING MISS CRAZY

Are you ready to be just a bit more daring, just a little more risqué? Well, after reading this chapter on going for a drive, whether it is you or your lover behind the wheel, I guarantee you the ride will never be the same.

So fasten your seatbelts for my friend Gloria's amorous adventure:

GLORIA

Rod and I often drive to our weekend cabin about three hours from where we live. Most of the drive is on an interstate highway, and it can get pretty boring. We've tried lots of word games, mind games, "can you top this" and "are you smart enough to keep up with me" kinds of things. But even they aren't too stimulating after a couple of hours. Anyway, I don't recall exactly how we first discovered the kinky pleasures of travel, but I think it started with a trucker who looked down at our passing car and my body. At the time, I was wearing only my bikini and my watch. He yelled some kind of good-natured, complimentary obscenity. He was driving a high-rise 16-wheeler. So his point of view enabled him to look down at the passing parade. It was obvious he was playing his own kind of game. Anyway, instead of just looking away, I glanced up and shook my breasts just a little in my skimpy top, which made him yell all the more.

Rod spun away, and I thought he might be angry, when all of a sudden, he reached over and pulled my top down, slowing up just enough for the truck to pull alongside again. The guy in the truck went crazy and almost drove off the highway. Rod laughed and accelerated the hell out of there.

My startled feeling was rapidly overcome by a feeling of being very wicked. I turned my head toward Rod and did my shaking number again, holding my bare breasts with my hands. I'm fairly well endowed so I had my hands full. I was humming a song and couldn't wait to see what he would do next.

It didn't take long. Rod's hand came across the seat again and my bikini bottom went flying with one tug. My God, I thought, here I am cruising down the highway completely naked. The ultimate flasher on wheels. What a sensation! Not exactly your basic little old lady from Pasadena.

We flipped my seat all the way back. The cars that were level with us hadn't a clue about what was going on. But when a trucker came into view, Rod would accelerate and close the distance. As we began to pass, he would slack off on the accelerator just enough to equal the truck's speed for a few seconds as we came alongside. What fun. I would writhe around and play with my breasts, seemingly oblivious to whomever was next to us. As Rod used his free hand to do his own thing, truck horns would blare, headlights flash, arms wave and all kinds of urgings and invitations were shouted. It's a good thing that Rod's car has the speed to leave any truck in the dust, because most of these guys went bonkers when they watched our performance.

Rod and I have refined this sport and find that it plays with a variety of costumes— skirts that I can pull up over my hips, halter tops

The ultimate flasher on wheels. What a sensation!

that I can pull down to my waist, a front opening bra...well, you get the idea.

After reading this chapter, I have a feeling that you and your lover might want to throw some of your sexiest outfits in an overnight case and run to the nearest gas station to fill your tank. But if you should run out of gas, don't worry. I'm sure your lover will be more than happy to give you some helpful and experienced roadside service.

CHAPTER 22

BON VOYEUR

L et's talk about the language of sex. I've always felt that two of the most erotic words in the vocabulary of sex are *voyeurism* and *exhibitionism*; as in watching and performing. I especially like the word *voyeur*. It sort of slides dangerously out of your mouth and sounds like it might inspire a voyage to some delightfully naughty place to enjoy watching something definitely risqué or even something risky.

Exhibitionism can be a multi-faceted eroticism, with the erotic thrill directly proportionate to what level of exposure you're willing to risk. Making love to each other in front of a window in a high-rise hotel is one kind of exhibitionism. Putting your hands inside each other's clothing while dancing in a wild disco is another. The result is a gloriously sensual feeling of nude swimming on a moonlit beach. Or perhaps something more subtle like whispering suggestive thoughts to each other during a chamber music recital or tracing a fingernail in sensuous paths on your lover's thigh at a dinner party as you're writing naughty words on his leg with your finger. All of these have different levels of exposure and risk as well as different kinds of rewards—from cheap thrills to thrills of a higher, more complex order.

Happily, exhibitionism is a two-way street and you don't actually have to show anything. The outline of an erect penis inside a pair of jeans can create a quiet sensation, and it's just the same for hard nipples showing through a skimpy T-shirt. Even a tiny bit of accidental exhibitionism can be fun. So share the view occasionally and indulge in the experience of some furtive flashing.

Such is the case with Sue's exhibitionist experience:

SUE

When I'm good, I'm very good. After a wonderful night of some innovative lovemaking and a late morning where my boyfriend Tom received my gift of breakfast in bed as the icing on the coffeecake, he promised he would indulge me in some of my favorite pastimes like shopping. Knowing there was going to be a new dress at the end of this rainbow only made me more excited. Even though it was a dreary, rainy Saturday afternoon, I couldn't help skipping through puddles and dragging Tom right alongside.

I found three sexy little numbers in the first boutique, and I couldn't wait to try them on. One tug in the dressing room and my halter top flew over my head. Another zip and my skirt was around my legs on the floor. Tom wanted to take a look and as he pulled back the curtain to my dressing room, I clutched one of the dresses to my bare breasts, not knowing who was invading my sanctuary. When I saw who it was, I relaxed and as I was shimmying into my dress, I noticed that the curtain was left slightly open and also that a tall, gorgeous guy in the shop was getting a peek. His lady friend was looking through the dress rack and this stud in the tight jeans was giving me the once over. I slowed down. Getting the tiny dress over

Even a tiny bit of accidental exhibitionism can be fun.

my hips didn't seem to be such a rush. Tom thought my posturing was all for him, and when I realized all of a sudden that two sets of admiring male eyes were taking in my every move, I was really turned on. I loved giving a sexy show for my boyfriend and if someone else was getting a teeny peek, oh, well. There didn't seem to be anything wrong with that. With a little flesh here and a lot of flesh there, it was a very torrid ten minutes.

As we exited the dressing room, my halter top and skirt securely in place, I pretended that I hadn't noticed my secret admirer. But as we were leaving the boutique, I couldn't help stealing a backward look. Quietly, unobtrusively, he blew me a kiss.

To take that experience just a step further, I'm sure you'll agree that watching someone having sex can be an incredible turn-on. Just check the line at your neighborhood X-rated video store. And have you ever watched a couple groping in a darkened theater or accidentally discovered people in the act when you blundered through the wrong door or walked past the wrong car? A bit embarrassing, perhaps. But while any of these things can give you a hot flash, being watched or imagining that you're being watched can make you just as hot. No, we're not suggesting that you throw open the windows in your bedroom and invite all of your neighbors to watch you and your lover in the throes of passion. There are far more subtle, wicked little substitutes—such as:

♥ The next time you take a trip together and are staying in a high-rise hotel, throw open the curtains and put on a show for anyone who might be watching from their room in the hotel next door or someone walking around outside who just happens to glance up at the right time.

♥ If you have friends who live in a high-rise apartment, borrow it for a weekend vacation getaway. Then open all the blinds and curtains, and try walking around in the apartment completely nude. Combine the two. Spend the entire day or weekend, if you dare, with your clothes completely off. Walking around all day without clothes is a wonderfully free, liberating and exciting sensation, sort of like swimming nude. And wondering just who else may be watching definitely adds to the excitement.

♥ If you're lucky enough to be traveling with each other on a train with your own private bedroom, open the window curtain and unzip for the viewing pleasure of the people in the towns through which you pass.

Here are my friend Carol's thoughts on the subject:

CAROL

Roger and I love to run off together for a weekend at some great hotel. We have three lovely children, but their presence can be more than an inhibitor to what Roger and I are free to do sexually. So we leave them home from time to time and we go and get romantic. Candlelight dinners, dancing, lazy swims in the pool at midnight. We also get hot, the kind of heat that a romantic, alone-at-last vacation ignites. Not your everyday lovemaking. We get crazy, we get theatrical and, best of all, we get wanton and wicked. Sometimes, we even make love in our hotel room with the lights on so that someone who just might be looking out the window of a nearby building can vicariously enjoy what we're enjoying. Now we never know for sure if anybody is actually watching, and chances are one in a million that anyone is really out there. But it's the idea, the fantasy of doing it for all to see that heightens the lustfulness of what we are doing. Don't get me wrong, we don't do this in broad daylight in a room on the ground floor of the hotel, and we save our performance for late in the evening when it's dark outside and only partially lighted in our room. We don't wave signs or flags, but we do like the feeling of thinking that someone may be watching. Roger and I even talk about what the other person or couple may be doing to themselves or to each other as they watch. That's sort of like a double dose of fantasy.

There is also a difference between dual exhibitionism in

which you are doing erotic things to each other and solo exhibitionism in which one of you is raising the pulse rate of a stranger who is watching you.

Tony's vignette about his girlfriend Eve is a perfect example:

TONY

Eve likes to wear clothes that show off her sexy body. I think she gets some perverse thrill when she sees me watching other guys watching her. If she does, then we're even, because it also gives me a thrill. It never fails to stimulate me when I see guys who are staring holes through whatever she happens to be almost wearing.

On the bus the other day when we sat down in one of the seats that run parallel to the sides of the bus, I got that old feeling that somebody was mentally getting off by watching my lady's movements, even though she was grabbing my arm and making it clear she was with me. Eve had managed to sit so that her dress was hitched way up and lace panties peeked out from the fork in the road where her thighs met. She was squirming slightly, crossing and uncrossing her legs, and each time she moved, her skirt inched upward just a fraction more. The poor guy on the other side was trying to be cool, but it was just about all he could do to stay calm. Eve's squeeze on my arm was growing stronger, and I could feel her heating up. She was doing quite a job on the guy and herself at the same time. Since I knew what was under the dress and the lace panties, it also did a job on me. We turned around and caught the next bus back to my apartment. Since she is such a wild lady, I think maybe we'd better stick to taxis from now on!

How many creative ways can you bring the suggestive words *voyeurism* and *exhibitionism* to life? That may end up being another book entirely. Bon voyeur!

CHAPTER 23

IN THE MOOD

One of the most empowering, gratifying feelings we can give ourselves is the confidence to know we are able to put our lover "in the mood." And what sinfully delicious fun it can be to explore the myriad of almost endless possibilities we have at our disposal in order to do just that. Usually, I call upon my ability to stimulate one or more of my lover's sensory responses, which I love to do because the rewards are so immediate and so worthwhile. I'll let you in on why this deceptively simple technique works so well.

In the movies, mood dictates everything and everything starts with lights. That's right. Lighting provides the most basic kind of theater, of set design. Not a bad start when you have designs on each other. If the lights are not right, you can forget about the camera and the action and the actors, and you can forget about a master print and about marketing and distribution. Without lighting, you can forget just about everything that might have been worth remembering. For you and your lover, lights are the perfect thing to use to set the stage and set the mood.

Lighting can set a mood or change a mood. Think about

soft lights and low lights, and then no lights. The possibilities and combinations are virtually endless. There are blue lights, red lights, green and purple lights, black lights, candlelight, flashing lights and flashlights. My favorite happens to be pink. Pink bulbs give off a rosy glow, soft, subdued and sexy, and make you look absolutely wonderful. And the better you look, the more relaxed and receptive you feel.

Of course, there are more than just colors when it comes to lighting. There are back lights, side lights and front lights, overhead lights and don't forget about headlights. Next time you remodel, have the electrician install strips of tiny lights sort of like Christmas tree lights around the top of your bedroom wall. An otherwise dark room illuminated by these strips creates an instant, romantic fairyland. Don't forget to install dimmers or rheostats near your bed.

Experiment. Try them all. Try them in combination. One of my favorite touches with lighting is to group a bunch of large, beautiful candles along one side of the bed and then watch the erotic shadows on the wall. The silhouettes thrown on the wall are shimmery and slightly indistinct because of the flickering of the candles and the constant changing of the intensity of the light that they emit. Add to that the intensity of the lovers' moving and changing body positions. If you're into fantasies, the shimmering effect is a wonderful embellishment.

Blindfolds can enhance your sensations...

And don't forget that candles are available in a variety of exotic fragrances, including fruity, floral, wooded musk and Oriental incense. If you run out of candles, use a colored bulb and spray cologne on a scarf that you then drape over the lamp shade. With the help of strategically placed sensuous lighting, the added beauty that you and your lover will see in each other's faces and bodies will not only delight and please your aesthetic sense, but will fuel the flame of your passion for each other. What better way to put your lover in the mood.

And since we've just been discussing the many pleasures of candles, I think the time has come for us to go on another erotic stroll with the understanding and acceptance that a bit of pain can be a pleasure. Now please don't be put off or afraid by a little pain—tiny or minuscule amounts that are guaranteed not to hurt anyone. Blindfolds can enhance your sensations when acting out this fantasy. Or you may choose to watch every second of what is happening. The choice is completely up to you.

The object of the game is to tease and titillate your lover by dripping little drops of wax from a lighted candle onto your lover's naked body. Ouch! But not really. The sensation of the wax dropping is similar to cold water dripping off an ice cube and splattering onto bare skin. One is hot, the other cold, and both produce a pleasurable sensation. As a matter of fact, combining the two sensations is not a bad idea.

In any case, there is really no unpleasant pain involved in dripping candle wax on your lover a drop or two at a time. The sensation is only momentary, but it does send a tiny, erotic jolt through the nerve endings of your waxed lover. If your lover is super-sensitive and nervous about the hot wax, you can mitigate the jolt by quickly leaning over to suck and lick the wax off your lover's skin which, by the way, can definitely add additional pleasure to the process. Or, you can first rub a spot with an ice cube, and then touch it with a droplet of wax, and then begin to suck and lick.

While on the subject of the many lovely uses of candles, let's shed some light on an equally erotic and no less practical use of wax. Many men are especially turned on by extremely smooth and hairless skin on a woman's body. For that kind of man, helping to get your skin just that way can be part of the turn-on. Following a shower or bath together, lay down on some fluffy towels covering the bed or the bathroom floor. Then let him do the honors of a hot wax depilatory. For those of you who have not yet become familiar with the sensuous joys of a hot wax trim, this is definitely worth trying.

Hot wax depilatory treatments are readily available at your local drugstore. One of our easy-to-use favorites is One Touch by Inverness.

A hot wax treatment can be a sensual ritual that dramatically raises hairs while removing others. Depending on your personal sense of the dramatic, a hot waxing can be favorably compared in staging and technique to the intricate discipline of a Japanese tea ceremony or to the lingering satisfaction of a five-course dinner at Four Seasons or Tour D'Argent. The point is that it can be auto-erotic art, an exciting experience. And like most experiences, practice makes perfect.

A secondary benefit of waxing can be a mild and exciting instruction for both you and your lover to the previously mentioned "a little pain can equal a lot of pleasure" principle. You will find that the stripping of the wax and the hair from her body creates a tiny flash of pain, just the slightest sting, which dissipates almost immediately, but which leaves behind a warm, tingly feeling. That feeling can be retained and enhanced by massaging the stripped area with your favorite body lotion applied with warm, soft hands. Then, back to the next application and sting. The next pleasurable stripping, again and again, until all the hair is gone.

That feeling of being groomed by your lover can take you back to a primordial place, an almost primitive sense of being; the way animals groom each other and the feeling of pleasure and mutual gratification they derive from the experience.

I invite both you and your lover to do just that.

CHAPTER 24

VISUAL
DELIGHTS

B eing able to watch a strip tease constitutes a visual splendor for almost every man. And with the advent of places like Chippendale's, women can now avail themselves of this splendor as well. How wonderful!

The first time I went to Chippendale's, I had to practically be dragged there by my girlfriends because I was under the mistaken impression that going there was corny and wouldn't really stimulate my libido. Well, dear reader, my experience was quite the contrary. After being in a room full of erotically charged, screaming women and visually feasting on one beautiful, extremely sexy, well-endowed, gyrating body after another, I was literally ready to rub up against a lamppost on the way home. In fact, I don't think I've ever been in such a rush to get home to my lover in my entire life. After rushing through the front door, I ran around the house in a frenzy trying to find him, screaming his name at the top of my lungs. Thinking back, I must have appeared like an over-charged locomotive racing up the stairs and into the bedroom. Luckily, I found him standing there with a slightly puzzled but pleased look on his face, and proceeded to throw him on the bed, literally jumping on top of him.

I learned several things that evening, not the least of which is how exciting it is to be the sexual aggressor with my lover. Another thing I learned is how horny the experience made me and how lucky I was to be able to return home to such a beautiful, sexy, responsive man. A third and quite interesting thing I learned was, even though my libido was totally stimulated by seeing all those gorgeous men, it was my lover to whom I was rushing home, my lover that I desired.

What a great revelation to experience firsthand that seeing other gorgeous, sexy men, either in person, on film or in magazines, not only did not diminish or replace my desire for my lover, but actually enhanced and stimulated it. Wait a minute, I thought to myself. If that's the case, not only am I not going to waste my time feeling even slightly threatened by my lover enjoying the sight of other beautiful, sexy women, maybe I should get him a subscription to *Playboy!*

The last and extremely helpful thing I learned was to do a great strip tease for my lover, which ended up being so much fun that I'm not sure which one of us enjoyed it more. And since turnabout is fun play as well as fair play, my lover has become great at stripping himself, easily rivaling the best of the Chippendale dancers. I urge you, dear reader, to tease and tantalize your lover into experiencing and sharing with you this uninhibited, sheerly delightful pleasure.

The great thing is that more and more women are discovering the art of stripping. My friend Jeri has some personal experience with that very thing.

JERI

Some nights after Dean and I get really stimulated, we like to strip for each other. If you have a guy who is as fit as mine, once you persuade him to strip for you, slowly and seductively and more than just a little dirty, you will forever know why those male strip joints are such a success all across America.

Dean loves to see me take it off for him, and I love to do it. I can *remember back when I was in high school always wanting to go to one of those "Amateur Night" shows at the local strip joints in our town. I didn't want to just go; I wanted to go and do it for the guys. To writhe, undulate and flaunt my body right into their sweating faces. To look down and see the lust in their eyes. To see them playing with themselves, wishing they could play with me. To do it so well that I would bring down the house, screaming, stomping, cheering and clapping. The whole nine yards. And bring home the $100 first prize. Every week. Just the idea of stripping clothes off my body in front of a bunch of men, all screaming and talking dirty to me, is enough to make me wet anytime. And make me hot for Dean! And with Dean, I now finally get to strip it off.*

Another variation we enjoy is to mutually strip. We get some hot music on our stereo system and then we dance together, little by little stripping each other. This tends to be a bit more of an active strip than when one of us does it for the other. As a matter of fact, when it is mutual strip night, we usually don't make it all the way through the strip. But that's okay, because having sex with a few clothes on turns us on as well.

Actually having sex with a few clothes on, and being able to rip them off in the process is quite a turn-on to more than a few of my friends. I am sure you'll see exactly what I mean, and exactly why, by reading some of their stories!

The first is from my friend Morgan.

...more and more women are discovering the art of stripping.

MORGAN

Don't throw away that old underwear or turn it into a dust rag. Wear it. Wear it for your lover. Wear it for your lover to enjoy ripping it off your body, that is. As a matter of fact, there may be occasions when you may be wearing new or expensive underwear

when you want your lover to rip it off anyway. Go for it. Rip!
Tear! And then tear into each other.

And, if you want sexy, with a tinge of roughness and tension, then
try undressing your lover without the formality of unbuttoning but-
tons or slipping off the slip. Just tear it away, and then have your
way with each other. My lover, Jim, loves to make love to me with-
out getting completely undressed. He just strips off a layer or two,
and then goes at it. Sort of a sexy caveman type. What I really love
in all this is what he does when he slithers down my body to kiss
and lick my vagina. He doesn't pull off my panties, he just rips
them right up the middle, and plunges in through the torn fabric.
What an animal!

BESS

My lover and I like to jog and work out together. He's always giving
me T-shirts to wear for these sessions, because when we get back to our
apartment from a long run or a couple hours of Nautilus, he literally
rips them off me! No shower, no nothing. He tells me that he loves the
smell and touch of my sweaty skin, and can't wait to get at it and
into me. As for me, it's a real turn-on being manhandled this way.

PAM

As an aerobics instructor and an amateur body builder, I am rea-
sonably strong. But Robert is even stronger and could easily handle
me physically. So it was a real surprise to him the first night that I
took him. As the aggressor, that is. As we began to kiss and stroke
each other, I just reached to his chest, grabbed his shirt with both
hands and ripped it up the front, buttons flying, and then literally
stripped it off of him, in tatters. Well, that got his attention about
my intentions!

DEAN

Jeri has a fabulous body. Exquisite, firm breasts with nipples about
the size of my thumbs. I mean, they really stick out. Below is a firm
stomach with wonderful muscle definition, and Jeri's butt is as
round and firm as her breasts. A major piece of body work.

I love to buy her T-shirts to wear around the house. They don't cost much, and they show a lot, but leave plenty to the imagination. And I don't mind that they don't last too long.

The reason they don't last too long is because I like to cut holes in the T-shirt with a pair of scissors. Where I cut the holes is my choice. A small, diamond-shaped hole over one of her nipples. Another long quarter-moon hole just under one of her luscious breasts. A medium-sized hole over one of the cheeks of her butt, and a big hole over her other cheek. Another cutout lets her pubic hair play peek-a-boo. A hole under her arm and behind her neck and at her waist. Watching Jeri walk around in my specially designed T- shirts is a visual turn-on of the first order.

Well, in order to implement some of these wonderful vignettes for yourselves, I suggest you save old, slightly tattered underwear for just such occasions, and in addition, stock up on a supply of inexpensive T-shirts. It may end up being the most pleasurable investment you've ever made.

CHAPTER 25

TICKLE
YOUR FANCY

Tickle. I love the sound of that word. Just saying it is pleasurable. Tickling can be so sensually creative. To begin with, it's not exactly a massage, not exactly torture, more like sweet agony. But exciting, yes, an extremely erotic delight that literally can take your breath away and bring tears to your eyes. As a child, most of you loved being tickled. It was happy and it was fun and it made you laugh. As a grown-up, it can be even more fun, and sexy. Now you don't have to go out and buy elaborate feather boas or ostrich plumes or Indian bonnets or cat-o'-nine-tails made of silk strips. You can go out and buy any or all of these, if you wish. But you probably have everything you need right in your own home. Try several sizes of her makeup brushes. A complexion or powder brush is particularly sexy, with a large head of soft, hairy bristles, perfect, particularly on the tip of his penis or his or her nipples. Other perfectly good ticklers include a silk scarf, a nylon stocking, a soft shoe brush or flower. Feathers, too, if you have a boa or ostrich feathers. And don't forget your tongue and the tips of your fingers.

When you're ready for more advanced play, we recommend

that you restrain your lover, which means to gently but firmly tie your lover up, blindfold him or her and then tickle slowly, slowly, languorously, lovingly, teasingly and titillatingly. Tickle some, then lick, then tickle again. Work on the most sensitive areas you can find. The biggest tickles come from the soles of your feet, behind the knees, inside the thighs, in the hollows of the abdomen between the hip bone and the lower rib cage, and on the sides of the chest. Wherever the sensitive areas are, I'm sure you'll find them quickly. But make sure to work on them with a variety of strokes. Build your lover's anticipation and excitement level. Then back off ever so slightly, letting the intensity drop off for just a moment. Then build it back up again. As the giggles turn to moans of pleasure, move the focus of your efforts to tickling your lover's genitals, first with a feather or complexion brush, then with your tongue and mouth. Once you are ready to go, you can go on for hours and hours, if your lover can last that long. Glide up and down the scale of erotic laughter and sexual tension with your lover. Do it until you both go crazy with pleasure. For one final tickle, here's Sue's experience.

SUE

Buddy has always been a real tease and nothing—or almost nothing—gives him more pleasure than tickling me. I have one of those silly, little girl giggles, but happily, Buddy gets a real charge out of it. Teasing and tickling. I thought I knew all about it. Right? Wrong.

One night after a few drinks and some sexy dancing, we got home late. I was so sleepy that I flopped down on the bed and dropped off. I woke up when I heard someone giggling. Surprise, surprise! I was the giggler. A naked giggler, spread-eagled on the bed, with arms and legs gently tied to our bedposts with what I recognized as my own pantyhose and a couple of Buddy's ties. Buddy was kneeling beside me, stripped and already hard. But what also got my attention was, of all things, what looked like an ostrich boa in his hand. And it was. What Buddy did with that ostrich boa for the next hour brought me almost to the brink of sexual insanity. He used the boa on my forehead, my face, my arms, along the sides of my breasts, on my breasts, over my stomach, down my thighs, on my feet and between my toes. Giggling quickly turned to laughter which ultimately turned to moans and shrieks. When I wasn't gasping for breath, I was begging and pleading for Buddy to stop. Thankfully, he knew I wasn't serious about the stop part. When Buddy finally took me, still tied, my orgasm was no laughing matter. We are talking welcome relief and complete release.

Believe me, Buddy has learned to laugh, too. And he sure looks funny wearing my boa.

Another way to explore, enjoy and continue to discover new and different ways to tickle and tease your lover is to let your hair down.

Whether you have a great, feline mass of hair or feathery little strands, it is an unmistakably stimulating, sybaritic experience to stroke your lover from head to toe ever so slowly with a beautifully sensuous sexual device that you perhaps overlooked and neglected, namely, your hair.

A hair massage will stimulate and affect different parts of your lover's body in different ways. I consider it to be a loving, amorous adventure to do some serious sexual sleuthing in the interest of discovering just what these different ways are. I suggest you stroke your lover over his face and neck, chest, abdomen, genitals, thighs, calves and, of course, down through his toes. Just when your lover is tingling and vibrating like a tuning fork, that's the perfect time to turn your lover over onto his stomach and slowly begin the whole, delicious journey again.

Remember to stroke your hair softly and gently all over your lover's body, from side to side, up and down, and in tantalizing little circles. If your hair is long enough, try whipping your lover with your hair for a surprisingly different sensation. And knowing how much we love giving our lover different sensations, try stroking your lover with wet hair. Let's say, for instance, after a wildly stimulating shower in which you both already began to go mad for each other.

Wet hair has a different texture which will give your lover a different tingle on your skin, a different excitement. Allowing the water to drip from your hair onto his or her skin provides a pleasantly cool sensation when you and your lover are both heating up to boiling point. Oh, I can feel the temperature rising just thinking about it. Cynthia has enjoyed some lovely, sensuous encounters with her hair.

CYNTHIA

Josh said the first thing that attracted him to me was my long, luxurious hair. He loves to run his hands through it when we're making love, and I soon got the hint that it could be yet another weapon in my sexual arsenal. I prefer washing it first and applying any creme rinse I can find that has coconut oil in it. Those Tahitians know a thing or two!

In fact, Josh is turned on by even watching me dry my hair because he knows what is coming next.

Smelling like something out of a Tahitian rain shower, I hair stroke Josh into silly putty. The amazing thing is that although I originally did this to turn Josh on, the act of drying my hair all over his face and body gets me right in the mood for some serious lovemaking.

Tickle some, then lick, then tickle again.

I love to kiss Josh through my hair, our mouths and tongues intermingling with the cascading strands. Looking through it, it's almost like a veil. It's hard to tell where my hair leaves off and our lips begin, and when my hair gets all tangled up in his stiff penis, smelling of Josh's heat and my coconut rinse, I can hardly stand it.

Something else I discovered, and this should encourage you girls who don't have long locks, is doing the same thing with my pubic hair. I recommend not trimming. The longer and silkier you can get your hair, the better. Try some creme rinse down there as well. Again, if you can keep your lover still long enough, try stroking him all over. Slide up and down his legs and arms. It's not so hard to do when you have him lying on his back. Tickle his toes. Straddle his chest and neck. Then tickle his chin and lips and nose. The trick is to get your man to just lie there and appreciate the sensation. Once they get the hang of it, they will gladly let you set the pace.

Josh has a picture of me in his office, and I made sure I gave him one of me looking through my hair. He says he gets an erection just looking at me and thinking of me. I have this fantasy of me doing a porno movie as the Breck Girl.

Perhaps you remember being in school and learning the word "onomatopoeia." I can think of few words that exemplify the definition of this rather strange phenomenon more delightfully than the word *tickle*.

CHAPTER 26

MESMERIZING MASSAGE

M assage. Just saying that word conjures images of spine-tingling, muscle-rippling, sensually stimulating, gloriously relaxing, totally pampering pleasure. Pleasure that almost seems to be a well-deserved necessity as well as a deliciously desirable luxury.

There are so many places from head to toe that are almost begging for that level of attention. So, with that in mind, I thought I would discuss with you a few loving and pleasurable methods and levels of massage about which you may not have thought.

Let's take our hands and fingers on a delightful stroll to, of all places, the eyes. Yes, the eyes are an extremely vulnerable and sensitive place to start our tactile journey. It's an area the massaging of which will engender a great deal of trust between you and your lover. Trusting each other is one of the best and sweetest of feelings that will help you thoroughly relax and enjoy the experience. Experiment on yourself. What feels good to you will feel good to your lover.

Take his head in your lap and begin by using your fingertips to lightly scratch and probe and press on your lover's head and scalp and forehead. Alternate firm fingertip pressing with delicate little circles across your lover's forehead and around the edges of your lover's ears. Take just one finger and, as lightly as possible, draw lines down the bridge of your lover's nose and lightly outline your lover's lips. Light little circles. Then begin the process of drawing closer and closer to your lover's eyes, which should by now be closed to reflect the absolutely relaxing aura you are creating.

Lightly draw the tip of a finger across your lover's eyebrows. Try to isolate and barely touch each single strand of hair, moving your fingertips backward and forward with the grain and against the grain of the hair, always using the lightest possible touch, which will tickle and titillate more than a heavier touch. Next begin to draw concentric circles around your lover's eyes, barely brushing the eyelashes and the lower portion of the eyebrow. Lightly, lightly, barely touching. No matter how lightly you think you're touching him, he'll feel an exquisite tingling sensation. Move away from and then return to the eyelashes, which can be quite sensitive. Again, don't forget to use the barest of touches, the absolute last layer of your skin on the fingertip. Draw small circles. Massage in endless concentric circles. Draw your fingertip across the eyelid from one corner to the other. Flick back to the eyelashes or the eyebrows, all the while with the lightest possible touch. Take your time. Repeat these rituals to your lover's content. A particularly pleasurable way to end the eye massage is to place your thumbs at the outside corners of your lover's eyes and then to press the skin down while you pull it away in opposite directions. That is, pulling the skin away from the center of the face and tugging the skin toward your lover's ears.

Now let's move slightly south to another small area of large sensitivity and great pleasure—your lover's nipples. No, it doesn't usually matter if they are of the male or female variety. Use the same technique described for the eyes: light, tickling touches. Wet your fingertips with your lover's mouth. Then, forming concentric circles and scratching delicately will immediately put your lover in an extremely responsive mood. Watching the nipples swell is a turn-on in itself, since it lets you know how much you're pleasing your lover with your sensitive touch.

When you or your lover are performing oral sex, one of the most natural places for the lucky recipient to place his hands is on the head of the other. Since head massage is high on anyone's scale of sensual delights, try using your fingernails to scratch your lover's scalp, then gently pull her hair and squeeze your way up to the top of her head, then down to the forehead. Do it slowly, just as slowly and lovingly and erotically as you are being aroused by the feeling of your lover's lips and tongue on your genitals, which by now is beginning to drive you mad with pleasure.

As you slowly move down your lover's body, remember that he loves to have his feet massaged. Ten million pedicures can't be wrong. If you haven't yet had a foot massage, find a good masseur or pedicurist and ask for his or her best foot massage. Then simply emulate their technique and add your own touches. Wash your lover's feet, wipe them, oil them, knead them. If you haven't made the connection before, you will discover a new erogenous zone—two of them, or maybe twelve, if you count toes. Insert your fingers between your lover's toes and give them a wiggle. Crook your finger around each one and pull slightly, stretching the joints and skin. Squeeze all five toes gently in your hand. Squeeze the heel a bit more firmly. Make a ball with your fist and push on your lover's soles and arches. Squeeze different areas of your lover's foot between the thumb and next two fingers. Gently tickle the soles. Make your fingers feel like angel's wings. Then oil the feet again and rub them inside a moist, warm towel. Wrap each foot and towel inside a dry one to keep the bed or fur from getting wet, and to keep them warm.

What to use for massaging, other than your fingers, hands

and mouth? Why not try a small piece of fur, the softer the better? You can purchase a fur mitt in one of those handy sex shops, or a stuffed animal covered in fur. Rabbit fur is wonderfully soft. You could also buy a pair of fur-lined gloves and turn them inside out. Just remember to keep it soft and smooth. Like my friend Joy's furry fantasy:

JOY

I never thought I would be a morning person, but Mark changed that.

He had recently brought home one of those airline in-flight sleep masks and as we went to bed, he asked me to put it on and sleep with it for the night. Since he had asked me to wear a blindfold during sex before, I wasn't surprised. In fact, I was turned on. My only surprise was that we just went to sleep. The next morning, I drifted out of my sleepy haze with a wonderful, light tickling feeling on my skin. When I couldn't see anything and reached for my face, Mark's hand stopped me. It was then I remembered his request from the night before.

Something was moving deliciously all over my body, but it didn't feel like Mark's hand. In my imagination, it felt like my body was floating along underneath a huge, fluffy cloud, and that the cloud was somehow making love to me. Sometimes the cloud would move in circles and sometimes in long caresses. I suppose every woman has had the experience of a man running his tongue over her skin, but this was like none of that. This was airy, frothy, light and erotically indefinable. Indescribably delicious.

I began to fantasize, to detach from everything but this incredible feeling. In my mind's eye, every tiny hair on my body was electrically charged, standing straight up, reaching for the sky, the sun and the moon. My mind wandered to another fantasy. I imagined that my soft blond hair had detached itself from me and was stroking me all over my body. The sensation was especially incredible on the soles of my feet and in the soft bend of my arm and along the sides of my breasts.

Mark bided his time, playing with me. He seemed to go on end-

lessly, sweetly and sensuously. Mark told me later that he was turned on by watching me while stroking and caressing me, watching my body tense and release, then tense and release again, listening to my breathing, prompting little gasps and groans. It became a challenge for him to bring me to orgasm without penetration or clitoral stimulation. Finally, mercifully, shatteringly, he did. By the way, I've tickled his fancy with a fur-clad hand on occasion, too.

Furry massages are a great and fun way to play, but for a serious massage, you need to use your bare hands. You don't need to be covered with a coating of body oil to get the best of your lover's attentions, however. Why not try it dry? A massage can be made equally erotic with nothing more than a fine dusting of powder. There is a wide variety of both odorless or exotically fragrant skin powders that provide a different kind of slippery sensation when applied to the body. Although powders don't work quite as well over areas heavily covered with male body hair, when on smooth skin, they do provide a sensation both equal to and different from the sensation provided by slick skin from oils and creams. Why not try Johnson's Baby Powder? For more fragrant and costly erotic massages, try the powder that's sold as a companion to her favorite perfume.

As a last note for those of you who believe a picture is worth a thousand words, we have something for you as well: two videos from Playboy— "Secrets of Euro Massage" and "The Art of Sensual Massage." Both are complete with nearly an hour of beautiful Playboy-type models demonstrating a complete manual of erotic touch and technique.

What feels good to you will feel good to your lover.

Whether you rely for inspiration on the videos or your own imagination, let your hands and fingers convey the language of love and passionate eroticism to your lover.

CHAPTER 27

GOOD VIBRATIONS

No matter how wonderful and stimulating and exciting the many sexual experiences you've shared with your lover are, there are times when—because of external pressures, stress or just plain exhaustion—your beautiful lovemate may simply not want or be able to make love. This is usually the time I count my blessings that I'm fortunate enough to be a female and resourcefully reach for my special pulsating pal, my buzzing buddy, otherwise known as a vibrator.

I remember one particular evening when my lover and I were lying in bed, and he was just about to journey into the Land of Nod. So I tiptoed quietly over to my dresser and took my friendly vibrator out of the drawer. Back in bed, I began to slowly and languorously rub it all over my body. My lover slowly opened his eyes and began watching, his curiosity quickly turning into fascination. I smiled at him and whispered that I was fantasizing it was his touch and his caress I was feeling. I could see that he was totally relieved not to feel obligated or pressured to make love to me that night. Feeling proud of myself at my thoughtfulness, while at the same time ensuring my sexual pleasure, I closed my eyes to continue.

I don't suppose you'd be a bit surprised to learn that my lover suddenly felt an overwhelming need to assist me, took the vibrator out of my hand and began massaging my clitoris with my reliable friend. His fascination increased with each movement of my body as he brought me to multiple orgasms.

Finally, exhausted, I drifted off to sleep locked in his arms. The next morning, I was awakened by my beautifully amorous lover who, after a great night's sleep, couldn't wait to make mad, passionate love to me. What a lovely way to start the day.

In closing, my friend Nadia suggests taking things in hand:

NADIA

A wonderful sexual experience came out of what started to be a small act of defiance. Normally, Terry enjoys sex almost as frequently as I do, but I do crave it more often than he does. Every man's dream, right?

Well, almost. In other words, outside of when I have my period, I would like to be having sex just about every night. But the pressures of business, client entertaining, late hours, reports and the rest often take their toll on Terry. He looks at the pillow often thinking how great it is to just snuggle in and fall asleep. Me, I'm thinking of snuggling him and doing everything—and then falling asleep.

My lover slowly opened his eyes and began watching...

The other night, we had come in from a late business dinner and Terry was eyeing his pillow again. Instead of getting crazy, I got clever and did something I'd never done before. I got my vibrator, quietly plugged it in and turned on my MTV. I did all this without a word. Then I slipped into bed, snuggled next to my sleepy lover and turned on the vibrator.

Terry was suddenly not quite so sleepy anymore. He watched through half-opened eyes as I massaged my neck and shoulders and then stroked my breasts and teased my nipples with the wonder wand. It buzzed, I sighed and Terry twitched. As I moved the vibrator lower across my abdomen, between my legs, I had Terry's full attention. All of a sudden, he was on top of me. He managed to get inside me just as I was ready to come to orgasm and we let out some pretty loud yells. Not unexpectedly, he fell asleep immediately afterward—but with a smile on his face. I snuggled up against his back, put my arms around him and passed out, in total ecstasy.

Just reading Nadia and Terry's story put a smile on my face as well. Try this and I have no doubt it'll put a smile on yours.

CHAPTER 28

VARIATIONS TO HEIGHTEN SENSATIONS

Within my own relationship, as my lover and I grow closer and more intimate, making love with him became such a wonderful experience, it never even occurred to me that sex could possibly get any better. Well, the amazing thing is that it most definitely can. All it takes is getting acquainted with and experiencing a few new sexual variations, some of which I learned from my lover and some from conversations with my friends and acquaintances.

The first variation is one which I've heard many times but never actually experienced until it was introduced to me by my lover. It's called a French tickler, which is an extremely erotic device that fits over the top or the length of the penis, and is usually made of soft rubber and contains strange-looking protrusions that extend outward all along its length. These protrusions may be bushy ones, spiny ones, spiky ones or even just plain ribbed ones. Whatever the shape, they provide a stimulating sensation in a woman's vagina that only multiples her pleasure as her lover is deep inside of her. You may experiment by positioning the tickler on the tip of his penis, in the middle or at the base.

Another exciting sexual aid is called a cock ring, which fits on your lover's penis close to the base. It is said to be extremely helpful in prolonging a man's erection, which, of course, prolongs the whole sexual experience. How perfectly wonderful!

These scrumptious devices can easily be found in any sex shop or in catalogues and magazines which contain ads for sexual aids and stimulators. If there's a sex shop to which you and your lover can go, I definitely recommend that you go together. The experience will be not only a delightful turn-on for both of you but also a tremendous amount of fun as you examine all the flavored sexual lubricants, creative and diverse styles of vibrators and other sexual appliances and enhancers, sexy lingerie, implements for slightly kinky role playing, erotic photos, magazines and videotapes. Sex shops are full of deliciously creative sensual delights that will most certainly add adventure and variation to your love life.

Two additional ways to enhance your lovemaking require nothing more than you, your lover and a place to make love. The techniques are extremely simple, but they provide enormous pleasure. The first one consists of both of you rocking your hips from side to side rather than thrusting forward and pulling back.

To visualize this example, imagine yourself facing and pressing against a wall. Your usual motion would be to move your pelvis and hips away from the wall, separating yourself from the wall, then moving back toward it, touching it again with your pelvis. But in this version, your pelvis never leaves the wall.

The only thing that moves away from the wall and your lover is first one hip and then the other. Using this motion, your pubic zones rarely lose contact and his pubic bone and the base of his penis will never break contact with her clitoral area. The rocking motion of his hips will maintain a continual pressure against her clit, creating the sensation of a side-to-side massage. The incredible feeling I share with my lover using this variation makes it one of my favorites.

While we're on the subject of incredible feelings, another surprisingly simple technique in the traditional missionary position will tremendously increase the intensity of both your orgasms. It is called the leg lock, and this time, it is the female who orchestrates the movements.

The technique is quite simple. As she feels her lover's climax begin, she wraps both of her legs around one of her lover's legs. In practically the same motion, she then should lock her legs together by squeezing her calves or ankles together hard, all of which increases the pressure on her lover's leg. The principal point of this is that the male leg is not the only beneficiary of the squeezing action. When she presses her feet or ankles or calves or knees or thighs together, she is also happily squeezing and tightening her vagina, which is an exquisitely pleasurable sensation to the engorged penis within and to her as well.

Speaking of giving both you and your lover pleasure at the same time, one of my favorite ways involves the use of the trusty vibrator I spoke of in Chapter 27. Picture, if you will, this scenario of you and your lover making passionate and smoldering love. After a long, sizzling amount of foreplay during which you use the vibrator on each other, your lover carefully presses the vibrator against your anus just before he penetrates your vagina with his penis. A little care is required for this one, but the buzzing and vibrating sensations will be strongly felt by both of you at the same time, and can create stimulation that will bring you to an orgasm equal to or better than any you have ever known before. And with that delicious thought in mind, I would like to close this chapter by sharing with you Celie's vibrator variation.

CELIE

I know a lot of women have this "thing" about vibrators. They think they're cold and mechanical—and that they wouldn't be able to have an orgasm with their lover if they got hooked on a vibrator. Well, I have a completely different point of view. It's true that when

I got my first vibrator as a gag present from a girlfriend of mine, it sat unused for over a year. I was slightly frightened of it, actually. I wasn't used to the idea of having control over my orgasms.

Paul was away on a business trip and I missed him desperately. Our sex at that point was great, but I had sort of reached a comfortable plateau. One night I noticed the vibrator lying in the drawer and thought I had better try it or get rid of it. Well, the first time was nice. No orgasm, but a very nice sensation. The second time I tried it, later that afternoon, I had an orgasm like I had never had before! Long and drawn out and so extraordinary that I was shaking.

A few days later, I thought I would try again and discovered that I could have orgasms in succession. The most I've had is five, one right after the other, over about a 30-minute span. I had made a major sexual breakthrough. Since I was in control of the instrument, I could come as I pleased, although I had never before been able to climax during masturbation. I felt powerful and renewed, with a new kind of sexual energy. I couldn't wait for Paul to come home so I could see if my vibrator education would renew our sex life. I was also a bit apprehensive because I was afraid that orgasm and vibrator now went hand in hand. I was anxious that maybe my climax with the most important person in the world would be different. Happily, this was not the case. All those orgasms merely whetted my appetite for more. Besides, I've learned what I like and how I like it, and I've articulated that to my lover. Paul immediately noticed the change in me, and I told him what I had been up to. He loved the idea and even asked me to use the vibrator while he watched—taking mental notes, I'm sure.

Paul went on to create a whole new vibrator experience for me—and for him. Now, when I'm sucking Paul, I use the vibrator

The techniques are extremely simple, but they provide enormous pleasure.

to caress and stimulate the area around his penis and testicles, and especially the sensitive skin separating his scrotum and anus. I also reach over and touch his nipples with the vibrator, too. All of this vibrating adds a much appreciated dimension to my oral talents. When I feel him begin to tense and tighten his muscles in preparation for climax, I turn the tip of the vibrator to his anus, pushing against it ever so gently. Paul absolutely explodes, an eruption of body, mind and sound. Sometimes it seems that he vibrates off the bed suspended in midair, all powered by that vibrator.

What a wonderful variation. So simple that anyone can try it, and yet so good. Thank you, Celie.

I would like to end this chapter by reminding you that there are dozens of wonderful mail-order catalogues from which you and your lover can order adult toys that will be delivered for your mutual delight. These erotically oriented catalogues run the gamut from how-to books to X-rated videos to miracle sex aids to lingerie for her and sexy clothes for both of you. These catalogues are advertised just about everywhere you look, most typically in magazines like *Penthouse, Playgirl, Cosmopolitan* and several others.

If you'd like to experiment with these catalogues by ordering only one, then I suggest the *Night Classics* catalogue. Their products run the gamut from a sleek boutique of luxurious lingerie to racy reading to erotic chocolates to kinky cookies to a complete offering of vibrators and videos. And most of these products are satisfaction guaranteed with a 30-day return policy. I feel that *Night Classics* is the best of the best, but here is a list of all my favorites in case you'd like just a few more.

♥ *Night Classics* (fashions to videos to sexual novelties)
   P.O. Box 8111
   San Rafael, CA 94912
   (612) 942-0635 or (415) 456-1800

♥ *Michael Salem's Boutique* (lingerie)
P.O. Box 1781
FDR Station
New York, NY 10150

♥ *Frederick's of Hollywood* (lingerie, plus hot little items for him)
6610 Hollywood Blvd.
Hollywood, CA 90028

♥ *Victoria's Secret* (lingerie and sexy clothes)
3425 Stelzer Road
Columbus, OH 43299
(800) 888-8200

♥ *The Xandria Collection* (sexual aids)
P.O. Box 31039
San Francisco, CA 94131

♥ *Adam & Eve* (sexual aids)
302 Meadowlands
P.O. Box 8200
Hillsboro, NC 27278
(800) 334-5474

♥ *Pink Pussy Cat Boutique* (everything sexy)
167 West 4th Street
Department 889
New York, NY 10014
(212) 741-1212

♥ *The Pleasure Chest* (everything sexy)
156 7th Avenue South
New York, NY 10014
(212) 242-4185

♥ *Playboy Products* (videos, lingerie)
  P.O. Box 809
  Itasca, IL 60143
  (800) 345-6066

♥ *Private Showcase Video* (adult videos)
  1004 Hope Street
  P.O. Box 4357
  Springdale, CT 06907

♥ *Leisure Time Products* (adult videos)
  P.O. Box M827
  Gary, IN 46401
  (800) 874-8960

You can find just about any catalogue you like, whether it be for sex toys, sexy clothes or erotic videos, and you can also get on the company's mailing list.

CHAPTER 29

SLOW
MOTION

U p till now, I've been telling you about the sheer
pleasure of being able to bring your lover to orgasm
in the most passionately delicious ways. Now I'm
going to show you how to prolong the pleasure till he or she
begs for mercy. Great sex with your lover can be tantamount
to a Kentucky Derby, the Indianapolis 500 or winning the
America's Cup. Or it can be the most sinfully scintillating
slow motion you've ever experienced. Variety is definitely
the spice of lovemaking. And giving your lover a variety of
feelings and sensations will allow you to give your lover the
sweetest agony of anticipation.

Now that you know how much your lover loves having his
nipples sucked or even his toes, while you're stroking his
penis, it's time for a bit more exploration. While you're giving the most incredible oral sex he's ever experienced with
your mouth and your hand, let your other hand caress his
testicles and then slowly move behind him to the area
between his testicles and his anus, and then around the anus
itself. Make sure your finger is lubricated and move ever so
slowly inside. Move gently at first; some men are reluctant
to be touched or penetrated in that area. But if you move in

slow motion, your lover will become less hesitant as he begins to trust that you only want to give him pleasure. Once he starts feeling that pleasure, he will relax into wanting more and more.

Remember, the fun is in being able to be the "love goddess" who can conduct the symphony, bend the note, sustain, prolong and delay the flow of the music—to tease, to control, to deny his release to the point where he is begging and pleading for the culmination of his orgasm. With all these delicious thoughts in mind, what better time to share with you my friend Sid's erotic adventure:

SID

Linda is very uninhibited. She loves to explore every inch of my body, and I love letting her do it. Since the first day of our lovemaking, she has made it clear that she is very oral. She simply loves to suck and lick my body. All of it. From end to end, endlessly. As you would expect, she loves oral sex. Mouth, tongue, hands, fingers, nails. I love to watch her move around my body. She loves being in control. My body is hers.

One part I can't see but love to feel is how she moves around my anus. There was some apprehension on my part the first few times, but there never has been any pain, only pleasure. Linda explained that by telling me she keeps her fingers well lubricated. She plays with me over the skin of my perineum, around my anus, then, with long, slow strokes, goes inside me. I had read for years about the erotic effects when a man's prostate is stimulated by a finger, but my experience with doctors, mine and the Army's, and the old "drop 'em and spread 'em" inspection routine, never let me give much erotic thought to a prostate. Linda changed all that. I couldn't testify in court to

...prolong the pleasure till he or she begs for mercy.

what she's touching or when. All I can testify is that it sends shock waves radiating out of some deep place inside me. At the same time, she's sucking my toes, licking my ears and whispering sexy thoughts, nibbling my nipples and on and on. It's like an erotic trip around the world.

She can do the stimulating forever, playing with me, teasing me, in complete control of my pleasure. Taking me up, then down slightly, then up a bit higher. When I finally come, after what seems like hours of pleasure, it feels like jumping off the World Trade Center in mid-climax. Linda leaves her finger gently probing and caressing inside my anus through all of this, and only when I've come down off the ceiling and am reasonably coherent does she slowly, ever so slowly, slide her finger out. If you have read about the aftershocks of an earthquake, try this and you'll know exactly what they're talking about.

I have tried it. Now it's your turn.

CHAPTER 30

FANTASY AND MYSTERY

O ne of the things I remember most fondly and most vividly from my childhood was playing "dress up," either by myself or with my friends. And when I played this game with my friends, you can be sure that I orchestrated elaborate Cecil B. DeMille–style extravaganzas. Although some of the scenarios and productions I created were a bit risqué, all my friends were more than willing to participate. It was a far more exciting and creative way to "play doctor." But memories of all that deliciously naughty fun needn't be quite so distant. As a matter of fact, there is every reason to create brand-new memories with your lover by tapping into our wonderful, childlike ability to create exciting fantasies—and then bring them to life.

As adults, we have practically everything we need to indulge our imaginations. If you like, you can costume yourself to be a king or queen and have your lover brought before you as your newest sexual slave; I like that one. Or you can be Tarzan and Jane, Antony and Cleopatra, a French maid and chauffeur, a jungle trainer with a wild animal, or a barbarian and a princess. Or any of the great lovers of all time.
    You could be Picasso with his lover, a beautiful new model,

or you and your lover could both be artists using each other as decorative canvases with swirls of body paint.

If you like, you could switch roles with your lover, making him up as a beautiful woman and making yourself up as a handsome man. The possibilities of this switch are endless.

Erotic fantasy role playing can manifest itself in so many delectable ways that you'll never run out of ideas. My friend Sandy was wise enough not to be threatened by her lover's fantasy, and actually helped him to fulfill it. Perhaps I should let her lover Rick explain it in his own words:

RICK

Now that I'm in my forties, I'm becoming more and more aware of younger women. And I mean really younger women. Like teenagers.

Sandy has caught me looking, and occasionally staring, at particularly hard-bodied and nubile high schoolers. You know, the high-butt cheerleader type. When she has caught me, her reaction usually is a laugh because she knows if I leave her for one of these young beauties, I'm going straight to jail; as in "Do Not Pass Go, Do Not Collect anything but a long stretch in the slammer." Shortly after she first noticed my under-age lusting, Sandy gave me a teenage treat of my own.

It began on a Monday night about a year ago. Sandy fed me a delicious dinner with a couple of chilled bottles of very good California Chardonnay. By the time I got around to watching the last half of Monday Night Football, I had a pretty good buzz. I was vaguely conscious of Sandy taking what seemed to be quite a long shower, but I was content to watch the game and to finish off the last of the second bottle of wine. Just as the second half of the game was coming to an end, Sandy walked in wearing a red-and-white cheerleader outfit, white sneakers and rolled-down bobby socks. You know, sweater and skirt and matching wristbands, the whole bit. And the outfit was about two sizes too small; in other words, skintight. The skirt was leather and fit her like Saran wrap. Her blond hair was piled tight into two ponytails tied with red and white ribbons on either side of her head.

My mouth must have fallen to the floor, because she started to gig-
gle. Reaching down, she yanked up the hem of her short skirt,
pulling it up to her waist, and exposing a freshly shaved, absolutely
bare beaver. That got my attention immediately.

"This little teenage cheerleader wants you to make love to her
sweet little teenage muff," Sandy whispered.

I immediately pounced on her, and it was a better tackle than
most I had seen on Monday Night Football. I had never seen a
mature woman with a shaved beaver before that night. The shock of
it was one of the most erotic feelings I have ever had. For a
moment, all I could do was look at it and run my fingers over the
smooth skin surrounding her vagina. I gently opened the pink folds
of her labia. The contrast of her white skin meeting the brilliant
pink of her vagina was an incredible sight. Sandy could tell how
turned on I was and this turned her on even more. "Suck my
teenage muff," she begged. "I'm a teenager and I want to be taken
by a real man."

Well, I did just that—and practically all night, too. Happily for
both of us, we have continued this game in different forms ever since
that first night. Sandy has performed the teenage cheerleader, the
babysitter, the runaway lost in the big city and on and on and on.

Sharing your lover's fantasy—and creating new ones—can
obviously yield exciting rewards. Combining fantasy and
mystery can also create an unforgettable sensual experience.
My friend Beth felt that her lover Tony was growing rather
distant and exhibiting a lack of sexual enthusiasm. She
found that he couldn't or wouldn't discuss the subject when
she brought it up, and he dismissed it as trivial, not something a couple should even talk about. So the next time he
came to her house, she didn't talk. She also had no lights on.
All he knew was that a door was opened, and then a perfumed hand attached to a perfumed body led him into the
bedroom. As they walked, he heard the sound of a zipper
and watched her dress slide away. Then one shoe and the
other were kicked off. Now he was being led by his beauti-

ful lover enveloped by the sound of her breathing, punctuated only by soft moans. Nothing else. No distractions. No talking, no lights, no music. Just rising sexual tension. But since this is Beth's story, I'd better let her tell it:

BETH

Tony and I had started off well, but he took it as a foregone conclusion that passion waned once a couple had familiarized themselves with each other's turf. I wasn't ready to acquiesce so easily. He planned to come over one evening, and as the doorbell was ringing, I had an idea. I wanted to see his reaction, to see if a moment could be captured through sensory deprivation.

I thought I might be able to take him out of himself if the circumstances were unfamiliar. Without any planning on his part such as taking a vacation or renting a hotel room. Without any surprises in terms of who I was or what I was doing. I wanted to take away the sights and sounds with which he had become accustomed and, subsequently, apathetic.

Since I didn't have this planned, all I did was keep the lights out and play it by ear. When Tony entered and asked what was going on, I was mysteriously silent. I reached out to him with my perfumed hand and gently caressed his face with my fingers. Slowly my hand trailed down his body, over his nipples, over to his arm, and led him very deliberately toward the bedroom.

...create exciting fantasies—and then bring them to life.

When we reached the door I stopped, and in the silence all he could hear was the sensual sound of my breathing as I unzipped my dress and let it slide to the floor. Kicking off my shoes, I slid my hand very provocatively across the front of his pants, over his penis and down the inside of his thigh. Letting out an almost imperceptible moan, I reached up, took his wrist and led him into the room. He was still muttering a few things when I seated him on the bed and took off his shoes, but I could see he was reacting to the atmosphere of mystery I had instinctively created.

It's kind of like having a discussion with someone who has lost his voice and, consequently, your own voice becomes soft and whispery in response. But this time, there wasn't even that.

Since the removal of his socks and shoes, jacket, tie and shirt also seemed to have some effect on the removal of his preconceptions, I knew he had at least decided to see what would happen. And since I was wearing nothing, as soon as I had removed most of his clothing, I softly and quietly moved closer to him, straddled him with my legs as he sat on the bed, and rubbed my breasts across his face. A gasp from him, and I knew I was on the right track.

I pushed him backward, caressed his mouth with one hand, took my nipple and rubbed it across his lips with the other. I was really enjoying this! I pulled back for a moment and let him watch me lick my own nipple before pushing it back at him, this time into his open mouth. I realized I hadn't even kissed him at this point, but since I usually would have started any sexual foreplay in that manner, I decided just to keep rubbing my body against his. Slowly, smoothly, seductively. The room was pitch dark, punctuated only by rapid breathing.

I began to suck his neck, his earlobes, his nipples, down to his navel, and continued down to his erect penis. At that point, it was obvious that Tony's interest, as well as his passion, was totally rekindled. Quickly turning into a super-sleuth, he examined every inch of my body as he gathered his clues and eventually solved the mystery in his own tantalizing way.

Thank you, Beth. I have a feeling that this is what Agatha Christie really had in mind all along.

CHAPTER 31

ADDITIONAL EROGENOUS ZONES

There is a uniquely exciting way in which my lover and I have unabashedly great sex. A way of which I wasn't really aware until he introduced me to its many pleasures. Looking back, I feel a bit naïve, but I didn't have any idea how sensuously delicious it would be to have my lover's beautifully sexy penis pressed between yielding breasts, as it slips and slides and glides back and forth, coming delectably and dangerously close to my mouth.

My favorite position is to lie on my back while my lover straddles my body. I hold my breasts together and adjust the pressure as he moves and thrusts his penis against me. All the while my mouth-watering lover manages to kiss me and massage my breasts, my neck, my shoulders, and slide his magical fingers into my vagina as only he can do. I can't even begin to tell you how much I totally adore my luscious, libidinous lover.

My friend Brigitte shared a similar experience with her lover Sven:

BRIGITTE

Like too many men, Sven thought having sex simply meant vaginal penetration. My breasts have opened up a whole new world for him. Don't get me wrong. We both love my vagina, but we find that having sex with my breasts is a sexy alternative.

I lie on my back and have Sven straddle me with his hard penis sticking straight forward between my breasts and nearly into my mouth. With the head of his penis so close to my face, it looks huge. Sven rubs a slippery lotion all over both of us—on our stomachs, chests, shoulders, necks and, especially lavishly, all over my breasts and nipples. He takes his hands in mine and we both push my breasts together surrounding his penis. As his hips thrust forward, pushing his penis through my breasts, the head pops right out in front of my mouth and I can lean forward to quickly surround it with my lips before he reverses his hips and pulls his penis back down through my breasts. Sometimes I quickly flick the tip of my tongue into the sensitive slit at the top of his penis, which gives him mini-shocks. One of the beauties of making love this way is that he and I can adjust the pressure on his penis simply by how hard we push my breasts together. As long as we use lots of body oil, it doesn't matter how hard we press because there is little friction.

When Sven is ready to have an orgasm, I slide down slightly to take the head of his penis in my mouth. I love it—and he loves it more.

I hold my breasts together as he thrusts his penis against me.

And we love just being able to hear about it. Thank you, Brigitte.

There is also another sensitive and sadly neglected part of both you and your lover's bodies, and that is simply your sweet little (or big) feet, and your toasty toes. Most people seem to forget that this area of our body is a remarkably responsive and extremely erogenous zone. Far from being alien creatures relegated to Siberia, feet are highly sensitive and most appreciative not only of our attention, but also of our creative and tender loving care.

In addition to being massaged, rubbed, stroked, soaked, tickled and oiled—as I described to you in Chapter 26—feet absolutely love to be kissed and licked and sucked. They also like to roam around and touch my lover's other erogenous zones, especially his genitals at the most dangerously risky and seemingly inappropriate times, such as in a restaurant, under the table, in front of other dinner guests, in the car while he is driving, especially in heavy traffic or stuck in gridlock, or while on a train, in a plane, in an elevator or waiting in line.

My own naughty feet just seem to have a mind of their own. But since it ends up being so much fun, I don't have the heart to chastise them. My lover certainly has no complaints, although sometimes I wonder which one of us is more risqué.

And speaking of risqué, I can hardly end this chapter without sharing the experience of my friend Barry, who is a connoisseur of both toes and feet:

BARRY

I don't know why, but having my toes sucked feels exactly like having my penis sucked, maybe better, because I have more toes. It sounds crazy, I know, but don't knock it until you try it.

Renee and I have a Jacuzzi tub and she usually starts in on me there. While I play with her under that perfumed, pulsating, warm water, she takes each of my feet and licks and sucks the bubbles off my toes. She runs her tongue around the outline of my toes and then flicks it in between, twisting and rolling it in delicious little semicircles. And this is just a fragrant prelude.

After we get out and towel each other down, Renee covers the lower half of my body with a light coating of body oil, then lays me down on the bathroom carpet or takes me to the cool smoothness of the sheets on our bed. Then she starts back on my toes, but with less flicking and licking, and a lot more serious sucking, the same kind of attention she gives to sucking my penis. While she keeps her mouth on my toes, she also slides her hands up over my thighs and grasps my penis, and when she grasps, I gasp. The culmination of her hand masturbating me while her mouth sucks and licks at my toes is an erotic equation in which one plus one equals about 3,000. By the time I have an orgasm I'm so worked up I really can't tell if it's coming out of my penis or my toes or some combination of all eleven.

Unleash the explorer in both your lover and yourself as you continue to discover new erogenous zones. Take a stroll over every inch of each other as you search for new ways to delight and excite. The journey is well worth it, especially if you discover new erotic terrain and stake your claim!

CHAPTER 32

SWEET SUBTLE STIMULATION

I t's hot, it's moist, it has a life of its own. It can make you squirm, slither, moan and groan. But it's also cooling and soothing. Sound familiar, or just confusing? Actually, it's quite simple. What I'm describing is your breath, your very life force. How potent is that life force? Well, how sexy was Lauren Bacall when she said, "Just put your lips together and blow"? The power of breath control probably originated as a sensual science with the Hindu practice of yoga and Tantric mantras. And it's still going strong, very strong.

Perhaps you're skeptical about the erotic effect of blowing your lover away? All right, let's do a simple experiment. Take the tip of your tongue and make a wet spot between any of your fingers, then blow gently on that wet spot. Feel that cool, tingly sensation. Then just imagine how your breath might feel on your lover's feet, high on a thigh, gently parting pubic hairs, on a nipple and caressing lips and eyelashes. A breath softly blown on the hairs of the back of your lover's neck, a puff of breath in your inner ear or filling up your lover's vagina with an enormous exhalation, then inhalation of breath, all are guaranteed to create intense responses.

A lovely, sensual surprise is to take your lover's breath away; that is, by sucking and then deeply inhaling your own breath during a long, deep kiss, for example. You will leave your lover breathless in more ways than one.

Here's another sensual surprise I think is stimulating. Just before you're ready to perform oral sex on your lover, fill your mouth with a few mentholated lozenges. Smith Brothers Cherry Menthol and Hall's Honey Menthol are both powerful lozenges and have the tingling mentholated and eucalyptus-like aftertaste. The pleasantly stimulating, lingering effect you feel in your mouth is exactly the same effect your mouth and tongue will leave on your lover's genitals.

Another sensation that leaves a wonderful taste in your mouth is that of ice-cold champagne. Just saying that word evokes a pleasurable response. Champagne will always make lovemaking feel like a celebration.

So with that in mind, I think it's an excellent opportunity to open that bottle, pour and lift your glasses in a toast to the splendor in the grass, the bed, the floor, the car, the elevator or wherever lovemaking is geographically possible.

While we're on the subject of geographic possibilities, it's time for you and your lover to throw off your clothes, pick up that bottle of champagne and take it into the shower. Now, the champagne needn't be icy cold, but the sensation of a hot shower spray delightfully mixed with the cool, tingly bottled bubbles is quite sensual.

Just picture the feeling of champagne bubbles flowing over your skin while you drink it, dribble it all over each other's bodies and slowly lick it off. How thirst-quenchingly delicious! Which brings to mind my friend Diana and her wet and wild adventure with the pleasures of champagne:

DIANA

I think Kevin first got the idea for a champagne shower from Piper Heidsieck and Gene Simmons—he of the rock group Kiss and reputed to possess a remarkably talented tongue. After one particularly wild evening when my lover and I had a lot to eat and even more to drink, Kevin popped the cork off one of our remaining bottles of champagne and put his finger over the opening, causing the champagne to spurt farther with a head of streaming bubbles. I grabbed the bottle from Kevin and reciprocated with a bubbly stream of my own. When we couldn't get any wetter or laugh any harder, Kevin picked up yet another bottle, then grabbed me and sprinted for the shower. Quickly stripping, we jumped in and turned it on. The warm spray soaked us both as he popped the cork and sloshed the bubbly stuff over my head. Gasping for air, I inhaled a mouthful of champagne and deposited my tongue into Kevin's mouth. The moment instantly changed from fun and games to, well, a different sort of fun and games.

As the bubbles poured down my body, Kevin moved with them, stopping at appropriate points for another and another taste of the champagne on my skin. He took another gulp from the bottle and held the bubbly in his mouth as he pressed his face between my legs. I felt the bubbles surround and tickle my clitoris. Then my immensely talented lover handed me the rest of the bottle and told me to pour it ever so slowly over my nipples and breasts, allowing a trickle of champagne to dribble down over my stomach and through the softness of my pubic hair, finally over his face and into his waiting mouth. The bubbles dribbling down over my skin, in combination with his flicking tongue, had my whole body exploding. My nipples were hard from the cold, tingling bubbles and somewhere, in back of my mind, I was also aware of the hot water stinging into my back and backside—an incredible combination of sensations.

The bubbles dribbling down over my skin had my whole body exploding.

Incidentally, it works just as well the other way. Champagne bubbles feel equally good on male or female skin, and the thrill of the bubbles caressing both of you can make for a special kind of happy hour.

CHAPTER 33

LOVE
POTIONS

How many times have you fantasized about someone who is totally, completely and heartbreakingly irresistible? And because it was your personal fantasy—where anything is possible—how many times did you have at your disposal a secret love potion that magically appeared, rendering the object of your desire helpless to resist you?

Well, as much as I would love to make your fantasy come true, I don't have a recipe for a potion that would make you smoldering enough to melt a glacier. But what I do have is a list of tasty tidbits that will definitely inflame the passion and enhance the libido. I'm referring to aphrodisiacs.

I can hear you saying, "Oh, that's just a myth. Those things don't really work." Well, you may be right. But then again, you may be wrong, and if you're wrong, how lucky for both you and your lover that being wrong is infinitely better than being right! So before you make your final decision, I'd like to enlighten you with a bit more information.

Aphrodisiac, a word derived from the Greek word for love and desire, is based on age-old traditions handed down through the centuries via folk legend, magic rituals, old wives' tales and, of course, wishful thinking. People have always known that combining rich, appetizing foods, reinforced with stimulating drink, consumed in a sensual atmosphere, unquestionably induces a euphoria. And that feeling lends itself quite easily to other sensual pleasures. As far back as 4000 B.C., the Babylonians were busily concocting potions to enhance their sexual powers. So the belief that certain substances can arouse and enhance sexual desire is just about as old as civilization itself. Some people vehemently deny that oysters—which vaguely resemble female sex organs—possess the aphrodisiac qualities legend has attributed to them. But others equally vehemently swear by them.

"Spanish fly," a powdered substance actually made from the outer shell of a small beetle, supposedly irritates sensitive body membranes, causing an itching sensation. One theory holds that when the itch is felt by a woman inside her vagina, she craves sexual intercourse to relieve that itch. But Spanish fly is difficult to come by, is actually illegal in most quarters, and can be dangerous taken in anything but very small quantities.

Another very risky aphrodisiac is absinthe. This liquor was used extensively as a sexual stimulant by the turn-of-the-century artistic community, especially in Paris. It is extremely dangerous taken in large quantities and cannot be imported into this country.

Figs are popular aphrodisiacs among the Greeks.

Alcohol in general, as Shakespeare says in *Macbeth*, "provokes the desire but takes away the performance." In moderate amounts, however, wine and other alcoholic beverages unquestionably lower inhibitions and heighten the libido.

According to legend, Napoleon was advised by one of his generals to eat truffles to increase his sexual potency. Truffles and mushrooms, magic or otherwise, are well known for their reputed ability to fulfill your wildest dreams. The ancient Romans were so covetous of truffles for their alleged aphrodisiac qualities that libidinous legions would ravage whole countrysides in order to obtain them.

St. Jerome supposedly forbade nuns to eat beans because they were regarded as a strong stimulant to the genitals. Seventeenth-century French monks were likewise forbidden to partake of chocolate because of its reputed amatory qualities. Chocolate does contain a pleasure-inducing chemical called phenylethylamine, which is the same substance released by the brain when we fall in love or feel a strong sexual attraction for that special someone. The heart rate is speeded up as well as the body's energy levels. No wonder there are so many chocoholics.

Many kinds of fish are reputed to be a potency aid as well as "brain food," because fish contains a great deal of phosphorous and other important minerals that may be considered long-term stimulants of the genital region. And for all you lovers of caviar, the benefit is reputed to be doubled for those fabulous fish eggs.

Among Mexicans, it is widely believed that the ground-up seeds and skins of avocados are enormously stimulating. The French think that artichokes, in addition to being a powerful aphrodisiac, have the power to prevent premature ejaculation. Also in France, a popular aphrodisiac drink consists of the yolk of an egg in a small glass of cognac drunk each morning. An Italian drink which has a supposed amatory effect includes wine, ginger, cinnamon, rhubarb and vanilla. Camel's milk mixed with honey, according to the Arabs, will cause a marked increase in potency. The Hindus believe that mint has aphrodisiac properties, supposedly stimulating the lower chakras, especially in men. If you can't get to India, try oil of spearmint, which can be obtained in most pharmacies. Hot and spicy curry, from a homeopathic point of view, may lead to a hot and spicy physical state.

Figs are popular aphrodisiacs among the Greeks. To me, the inside of a fresh fig looks remarkably like a beautiful vagina. Bananas, likewise, are yet another fruit presumed to be a sexual stimulant, hopefully not just because of the phallic shape.

Spices highly regarded for their aphrodisiac properties include basil, anise, garlic, ginseng, bee pollen (the dark variety of beeswax) and nutmeg (the latter is prized in the Orient as an aphrodisiac, especially among women, though it can be dangerous when taken in large quantities). Vanilla, a diminutive of the Latin word for "vagina," is high on the list, both ingested and also worn; vanilla oil is a powerful sensual fragrance, as are patchouli, sandalwood, ylang-ylang, jasmine and rose.

The use of an aphrodisiac seemed to be implemented in strange ways in English medieval times. It is reputed that a young girl would knead a small piece of dough and then press it to her vulva. The resulting baked mold would supposedly make an impression on the man of her choice.

Luckily, through the centuries, women have found far more effective and extremely sensuous ways to please their men with baked goods. Some of my favorites are the creative, as well as erotic, cakes you can order from erotic bakeries in some of our larger cities. These deliciously seductive cakes depict various erogenous zones and/or sexual organs.

So with all this information, the time is absolutely right to make your lover an irresistibly sensual dinner using any of the ingredients mentioned in this chapter. My final suggestion for this delectable dining experience would be a mouthwatering dessert which would most certainly include chocolate and vanilla. Bon appétit!

CHAPTER 34

BLISSFUL BEDDING AND COZY COCOONING

O ne of the things I absolutely love, but seldom have the luxury of doing, is staying in bed with my lover for 24 hours of pure pleasure. Due to our busy schedules, it's something for which we have to fight to make time, but the rewards are totally worth the struggle.

What makes this experience so delightful is that you get to shut out the outside world, with all its responsibilities and obligations, and do nothing but simply luxuriate in each other. And the best way to do that is for both of you to stay in bed and not get up, except when absolutely necessary.

If you can manage to sneak away to a hotel for this marathon, you won't even be bothered by uninvited guests, and the sole purpose of the telephone can be to order room service. How heavenly!

Equally heavenly is the time you'll have to simply relax with each other, sharing your thoughts and your feelings, being affectionate, feeling each other's closeness and intimacy and having pure, unhurried, uninterrupted, great sex. What could be better? Absolutely nothing!

One of the things I love to experience with my lover in the afterglow of lovemaking is something called cocooning. I have a feeling, dear reader, that you would enjoy it as well.

Picture a cocoon as a warm, safe place to snuggle up, surrounded by a soft barrier against the outside world, an enveloping, secret haven for just you and your lover, a haven you make into a sensual heaven. And how does one create this cozy cocoon? Quite easily.

Build it out of pillows. As many pillows as you can find. Regular bed pillows, couch pillows, floor pillows, throw pillows, baby pillows and pillows you haven't thought of. Stack them all around you, a harem-like billow of pillows. Then get comfortable. Get close and pull the sheet and pillows up over both of you. Completely cover both of you, from toes to head. Now you're cocooning.

Inside your cocoon, envelop yourselves in each other. Cushioned by the pillows surrounding you, your bodies will more easily join as one; they'll flow together, with the covering sheet over you protecting and filtering out any harsh or otherwise unwanted light. Staying with your lover in the cocoon for long periods of time can become slightly disorienting. It's easy to get lost in love and in lust. So jump into some sheets and pillows and cocoon the day away. But before you do, please read about my friend Lauri's cozy cocooning.

LAURI

Sam is a morning person—in every way. I'm not. I prefer sex at just about any time other than when I wake up. Maybe it has something to do with feeling that I look like a wreck. Maybe it's the fact that I feel better after a shower. Maybe I've got in the back of my mind that TV commercial lamenting morning breath. For whatever reason, I don't find the harsh reality of daylight conducive to setting the mood for sex.

Inside your cocoon, envelop yourselves in each other.

Sam and I discussed this, and he was considerate and understanding of my quirkiness. But one morning after I had showered, he asked me to come and lie down with him, which I willingly did. I love to snuggle with him, and this seemed as good a time as any. He pulled the sheet right over the top of us and took me in his arms. He kissed me. Just kissed me. And kissed me some more. All of a sudden, I became aware of the fragrance of my clean body and how his "slept-in" morning musk began to blend pleasantly. We were encased in a golden glow created by sunshine on the outside of our yellow-tinted sheets. I felt warm, protected. There was no interference from the outside world, just our bodies moving together.

Sam pulled the pillows down around us. Everything looked different under the sheets. There was no up or down. There was a sense of complete seclusion, of a certain unreality. The sheets and pillows enclosed and amplified the sound of our lips and tongues moving together. Also amplified was the rustling of the sheets as we moved on and under the soft cotton fabric and the sexy sound of Sam entering me and sliding in and out. I heard my own breathing, not just Sam's. I heard a moan. Was it Sam or me?

You guessed it. Morning is now my favorite time. Sam has even been late to work a few times, so we'll probably have to ration our newest activity just a bit. One last thing: It's best to use beige or yellow or peach sheets. You don't glow with the flow with dark sheets; you want a twilight rather than a repeat of the night.

Well, whether you cocoon with your lover in the morning before work, or during a magnificent 24-hour marathon, it's always a delightfully intimate experience.

CHAPTER 35

LIMO
LUST

Whenever I mention the movie *No Way Out* to any of my friends, they invariably say, "Remember that great scene in the limo?" In fact, even if the rest of the film virtually disappears into obscurity, the limo scene will continue to be a sensational memory to everyone who has watched that delightfully steamy encounter.

And why is that particular memory so appealing? Well, in addition to the spontaneously smoldering sex, there is also the added luxury and excitement of simply riding in a limo, the deliciously naughty pleasure of the possibility of being caught in the act—and the displacement of time and place that occurs when you make love in a moving vehicle: in limbo in a limo.

All of these delightful elements combine wonderfully into an adventure that both you and your lover should definitely experience.

Just hearing the word *limo* evokes the memory of a scintillating story from my friend Risa:

RISA

One afternoon my boyfriend Jimmy called me at work and told me he was taking me to a new restaurant that evening and asked me to dress "racy." I said I'd love to, so he said he'd pick me up at eight.

I met him at the door in a bustier top, micro-miniskirt, black stockings, garters, lacy panties and stiletto heels.

Beaming with approval, he led me to a sleek black stretch limo. Waiting by the door was an equally approving uniformed driver who smiled and beckoned us to enter his luxurious domain.

As we sank into the opulent black leather seats, I slowly looked around, savoring the smoky dark windows, slide-back moonroof, well-stocked bar, concert-quality stereo, cassette player and color television.

Jimmy handed me my favorite drink and pressed the button to close the roll-up divider panel, but left it one-quarter of the way open. After putting a tape of some cool and sexy music into the cassette player, he turned and began to devour me, first with his eyes, then with his mouth and tongue.

Just when I was about to rip my clothes off, the limo stopped, having arrived at a most beautiful restaurant that overlooked the city. The driver assisted me out of the limo, looking a bit flushed from what I'm sure he had seen in the rear-view mirror and said, "I hope you enjoy your dinner."

Jimmy and I enjoyed a romantic dinner looking out over the city lights. When it was time for dessert, we ordered chocolate mousse pie with raspberries and Jimmy told the waiter we would like it to go.

Spreading chocolate mousse all over his penis was great fun...

Sliding back into our limo, we drove around the city kissing and groping and sipping our drinks. Reaching over to the other seat, Jimmy told me it was time for dessert. He unwrapped the chocolate mousse pie and began feeding and kissing me. Then he slid down to the floor, removed my panties, spread my legs and slowly smeared chocolate mousse on my vagina.

I could barely contain myself as he expertly

licked it off, giving me the most wonderful orgasm.

When I recovered, I decided that he should have his just-desserts and proceeded to pull down his pants and boxers. Spreading chocolate mousse all over his penis was great fun, but it was even more fun to lick every bit of it off and give him the same incredible orgasm he gave me.

Just then, we arrived back at my apartment, so Jimmy and I quickly dressed.

As we said goodnight and thanked our very discreet limo driver for a great evening, he smiled and thanked us for the same thing!

Arm in arm, we watched him drive away and walked quickly inside to finish what I considered to be an unforgettable night on the town.

Just reading this story should boost limo rentals to new heights. My lover and I were definitely inspired to do the same thing—including dessert!

CHAPTER 36

RUNAWAY TRAIN

While we're on the subject of wonderful ways to travel, perhaps some of you can recall the movie *North by Northwest* with Cary Grant and Eva Marie Saint romantically touring the countryside in the sleeping compartment of a train. What fun it is to conjure up the excitement and fantasy of the incredible possibilities that can be experienced and the tasty new avenues that are just waiting to be explored.

There has always been a romanticized mystique about trains. They're the last of the great, graceful ways to travel in the modern age. Not only can we travel all across America, through the sweep of the Rocky Mountains and the Tetons, but also through the wine country of France and the valleys of Switzerland and on the Orient Express and the bullet trains in Japan. And these journeys all share the same characteristics: power and movement, plus a sexy combination of intrigue, romance and mystery. Tons of steel rocketing through the countryside. Whistles wailing in the night while the floor moves slightly to and fro beneath you. It's a constant, almost hypnotic rocking movement, similar to the movement of lovers' hips when they're moving slowly together. Picture a cozy sleeper cabin with a pull-down bed made up and the countryside rushing by outside your window. The sounds of trains passing in opposite directions. This has to be the ultimate in sensual coming and going.

When you and your lover are looking for a relaxed, romantic way to get away together, think about traveling by train for an overnight or weekend adventure. No matter where you live, there is likely to be a train nearby going somewhere. Think about how lovely it would be to see a bit of the countryside, dine on what can be surprisingly good food and wine and then stroll leisurely back to your private sleeper and make mad, passionate love on the rails.

And around the world, two of the classier examples of this fantasy-inspiring romance on wheels are the nostalgic Istanbul Orient Express in Europe and the American-European Express which runs between Chicago and Washington, D.C. These trains are simply elegant. You will be surrounded by wood paneling, leather, plush carpeting, plus china and crystal in the dining car, all the while being pampered by highly trained, attentive and fully uniformed attendants. Your choice of attire can range from casual to best of black tie. For those of you who choose to mix in a little business with your pleasure, cellular phones and fax hook-ups are available on most of the first-class inter-city trains.

Jean-Claude, who likes his travel the French way, shares a personal vignette which we'd like to share with you:

I literally have to stop myself to keep from exploding.

JEAN-CLAUDE

Colette and I take at least two holidays by train each year. Walking through the station toward the train, we're in a world of our own, carried along by the flow of our fellow travelers. A compartment paneled in walnut with beautiful brass and stainless steel fixtures awaits us. Mirrors always cover at least one of the walls, and the day couch pulls down into a cozy bed. We take a late dinner in the dining car, three or four courses, always served with our favorite champagne. Not one bottle, but two. The remains of the second we take along as we stroll back to our own private compartment. As I latch and bolt the door, Colette raises the shade on the window and we can see lights flashing by outside, sometimes glistening off the snow or a lake. The lights in our compartment are off and the only glow in the room comes from our bodies as we slowly strip each other. We watch our bodies reflected in the glass of the window and in the wall mirror. The train moves and we move with it. The sounds and the motion are fantastic, lulling us as we caress each other. We hold each other tightly as the train speeds rhythmically along its course. The feeling between us is even more romantic than passionate as we kiss each other slowly and longingly. But the heat of our bodies pressed together begins to inflame us and ignite our passion. It's almost as though we don't want to unlock our embrace, even to remove our clothes. I reach my arm down under Colette's skirt and rip off her panties. Fiercely, she reaches down, undoes my belt, pulls down my zipper and practically tears off my pants. "I want to feel you inside of me," Colette whispers. "Give it to me now! I want all of you!" I thrust myself inside of her as her warm wetness envelops me. I literally have to stop myself to keep from exploding. I catch my breath at the overwhelming emotions she arouses in me. Looking deeply into her eyes, I begin to thrust harder and harder and deeper and deeper into this mystery that is Colette. Feeling every sensation, every movement, she bites her lip to keep from screaming.

Just as we begin to build toward orgasm, I turn her body over and lift her to her knees. Her screams are muffled by the pillow as I thrust deeper and deeper inside her warmth. Nibbling and biting her neck in back, I feel totally primordial, like an animal as I hear her muffled sighs and moans. Turning her onto her back, I look into her eyes again and feel her lips and tongue caressing mine, waves of pleasure engulfing us as we tremble and shudder with the intensity of our orgasm.

Totally spent, the last thing I recall is drifting off to sleep to the sound of the train gliding swiftly along the track.

There are hundreds of ways to make love on a train as it moves through the dark. What a lovely challenge to find even more.

CHAPTER 37

ROMANCE ON A HIGHER PLANE

In the past, flying for me was hardly anything more than a means to an end, a way to get from Point A to Point B. The closest I ever came to encountering anything remotely erotic was either reading a steamy novel or watching a sexy love scene in whatever movie the airline was showing. I felt as though I had a winning Lotto ticket if I spotted someone sexy with whom I could make flirtatious eye contact on my way to the restroom. The usual scenario was one in which I would be seated either in front of or directly behind screaming quintuplets, or next to someone who snored loudly enough to vibrate the wall of the aircraft. But even that was a welcome change from my flight next to a woman who had so many health problems that she had to have memorized the entire *Physicians' Desk Reference* and felt an overwhelming need to share the wealth of information.

Needless to say, my experiences hardly lent themselves to my feeling that an airplane was a potential hotbed of erotica. But being the determined and resourceful individual that I am, I felt that a weekend flight to New York with my lover would be the perfect time to be creative. We booked a night flight so we could take advantage of that wonderful time when the overhead lights are turned out for the passengers to either watch a movie or try to get some sleep.

We drove together to the airport, but upon reaching the terminal, we pretended we were strangers and boarded the plane separately. Although we chose not to sit together, we sat closely enough so that we could steal furtive glances at each other. When I decided to go to the bathroom, my lover left his seat to walk in the same aisle, but in the opposite direction. Needless to say, when I tried to pass him in the aisle, not only did he make no attempt to get out of my way, but he made it as difficult as possible for me to get past him. My knees became so weak as he rubbed up against me seductively that I almost wanted to grab him right there. But I continued to the restroom as though we had never met.

Luckily, the seat next to his was empty, so on the way back, I leaned over his seat and said, "Excuse me, I believe you dropped this." I held out my closed hand, slowly dropped my black lacy G-string panties in his lap and continued on back to my seat. A while later, he walked past my seat with a magazine which he ever so conveniently dropped in front of my feet. I, of course, was delighted to reward him with a most provocative view as he slowly leaned down to pick it up, making him doubly happy that I had decided to give him my panties earlier.

...he reduced me to a quivering mass of jelly that practically melted into the upholstery.

After waiting for what seemed like an eternity, I walked over to where he was sitting and asked if I could sit in the vacant seat next to him so I could have a better view of the movie that was about to start. He smiled and said, "Of course," just as the lights were being lowered.

I attempted to watch the movie as he began moving his hand up the inside of my thigh. Biting my lip, I could barely remain silent as he began rubbing my vagina the way no one else can do. Placing the blanket over our laps, he slid down his seat, put his head under the blanket and proceeded to perform some of the most devastatingly intense oral sex I could possibly imagine, until he reduced me to a quivering mass of jelly that practically melted into the upholstery.

When I was finally able to stop shaking, I decided to do some undercover exploration of my own, and discovered a most beautiful sex organ that was in dire need of attention. I found it an incredible turn-on to kiss and lick and suck my lover's penis until he was absolutely ready to explode with pleasure, but had to contain his verbal outburst by biting on his own hand!

Somehow, through all our maneuvering, we managed to accidentally press the call button for the stewardess, who came over just as we had finished to ask if we needed anything. Giggling like two naughty children, we looked at each other, then smiled at her, saying, "No, thank you. We're just fine. We don't need a thing."

Looking back, our flight was not only the fastest I ever experienced, but also by far the most exciting. Air travel will never be quite the same again.

Now, for a slightly different but equally smoldering experience while flying the friendly skies, here is Sarah's airborne adventure:

SARAH

The best sex I ever had was with a beautiful Frenchman named Pierre on a long flight from Paris to Montreal. As you probably know, that's a daylight flight, and doing it in the daytime is always more dangerous than doing it in the dark. Flying dangerous. What a trip! We had lucked into a first-class upgrade on a much oversold flight. Pierre and I spent the first couple of hours drinking champagne and eating that great Air France food. But after a couple of hours of caviar, bubbly and suggestive talk, we were ready to take things a bit further.

I went to the restroom and Pierre played Mr. Casual, walking around the cabin a bit trying to throw the stewardess off the scent. I stayed in the washroom with my eye glued to the slit in the folding door, and when I saw Pierre arrive, I pulled the door open and he jumped in. I already had unbuttoned my blouse. It took me about a second and a half to get Pierre's belt loose and his fly open. He cupped my derriere and boosted me up on the wash counter to give himself a better angle on both ends of my body. On this Air France 747, two walls were covered with mirrors, which gave both of us a great close-up of what was happening.

With me sitting and Pierre standing, he could simply rock his hips back and forth, pushing in and out of my vagina while his fingers played with my breasts and my clitoris. The view was as wonderful as the feeling.

When it was Pierre's turn, I slid off the counter and sat on the top of the toilet. This position put my mouth right in front of Pierre's hard penis. He smiled and moaned with pleasure as he looked down at me and admired what I was doing to him. Again, the view was "airotic." The whole idea of this tiny space plastered with mirrors was an incredible visual turn-on.

Even after all of this, we still had six hours to go to Montreal. Air France showed two movies. Neither Pierre nor I saw one of them. We were too busy taking return trips to the bathroom—getting sky-high on each other's heavenly bodies. Vive la France!

Well, darling ones, the next time you see or hear any slogans for our many delightful and dependable airlines, such as "Fly the Friendly Skies," "Something Special in the Air" or "Takes You Where You Want to Be," I'm sure they will have a far more significant as well as pleasurable meaning.

CHAPTER 38

SOMETIMES LESS IS DEFINITELY MORE

What exactly do I mean by less is more in sex? How can that be? Well, allow me to elaborate.

For me, it began one night when my infinitely creative lover decided to approach our lovemaking with a slight variation. During the prelude to actual intercourse, he lightly explored every area of my body in that artfully passionate way that he does so well. At that point, he usually smiles knowingly as he feels me quivering like a bunny and simply melting under his caresses. That night, as I was practically begging him to ravish me, he pressed his luscious lips against my ear and whispered, "Tonight, I'm going to make love to you just a bit differently." "Oooh…tell me, what, what?" as I grabbed him and pulled him close to me.

He laughed and shook his head, whispering again in his seductive voice, "Listen carefully and do exactly what I tell you." I nodded quickly as my heart began to pound. "Take your arms away from me and place them against your body. Now spread your legs ever so slowly and just let me look at you."

My heart was beating wildly now as I readily complied with his request. Lying there, I felt his eyes move slowly over every single inch of me. He leaned over my trembling body and whispered that from this moment on, we weren't allowed to touch each other anywhere—anywhere except one place. Knowing exactly what that one place was, I shivered uncontrollably and whispered, "Please, please, give it to me now! Don't make me wait any longer!" The few seconds he waited while he watched me go crazy seemed like an eternity. It seemed as though the more he waited, the more I wanted it.

Finally, I felt his penis begin to enter me and I thought I was literally going to explode. Every move, every thrust, every nuance seemed to be heightened because I had to just lie there, unable to use my hands or my mouth. I almost begged for relief as my lover brought me to the most exquisitely fulfilling orgasm. Needless to say, this new way of making love has become one of my favorites and the expression "less is more" will never sound quite the same again.

On that note, I would like to end this chapter with my friend Mike's variation on "less is more" from his masculine perspective:

MIKE

Some nights, Paula and I invoke what we call the touchless sex rule. This tends to drive her nuts on several levels. First, I don't let her touch me anywhere. Complete denial. Second, I touch her only with my penis and my tongue. Because all she can feel are my penis and tongue simultaneously penetrating her vagina and her mouth, the sensations of being penetrated are heightened tremendously. The effect of sound is also heightened. The sound of my tongue licking her mouth and her mouth sucking my tongue adds an extrasensory turn-on to the proceedings.

...the expression "less is more" will never sound quite the same again.

Sometimes Paula loses control and reaches out for my body. When this happens, I take her by the wrists and hold her hands pinned down over her head. This probably creates a mental suggestion or fantasy of rape. I don't know that everyone considers quasirape a happy attitude in sex between couples, but as long as we are play-acting, for Paula and me, it adds an extra edge as we reach orgasm. Oh, and watching Paula squirm with pleasure and shiver with delight makes me want to do it all over again.

Hmmm—how many other ways can I prolong that sweet denial, that luscious tease?

CHAPTER 39

TATTOO FOR TWO

It has been said many times that our body is our temple. I couldn't agree more. I totally believe that our bodies should be nurtured, cared for, developed and respected. After all, we're not used cars that can be traded in for newer and better models. Not yet, at least! Therefore, we should deal wisely and carefully with the bodies we've been given.

Now, that's not to say we can't be a bit creative here and there in terms of decoration and ornamentation. Down through the centuries, a tremendous array of extremely diverse cultures have expressed themselves artistically by using their bodies as a most interesting and exciting canvas.

In today's world, the art of tattooing has proliferated to the degree that people who would have never entertained the thought of ever getting a tattoo are eagerly planning and deciding what their next tattoo will be.

Gone are the days when tattoos were a sailor's colorful companion to a horrendous hangover. On the contrary, they have become a personal and sometimes intimate means of expression.

Expressing oneself via a tattoo doesn't have to mean having a portion of the Sistine Chapel replicated on your torso or a king cobra coiled around your body from neck to ankle. Tattoos can be as tiny and as delicate as you like, and as diverse as your imagination can encompass. Traditional roses, hearts and butterflies are lovely, but tattoos can be far more individualized, such as symbols of happiness, good fortune, strength, peace and love, or symbolic art that is much more arcane.

Secret messages and obscure imagery that is understood and shared by you and your lover create an extremely emotional and intimate link between the two of you. But please be aware that tattoos, whether they are meaningful and aesthetic, light-hearted and funny, are rather permanent, so I would suggest staying away from specific names or initials displayed on prominently seen areas of your body. I say this only because past experience has shown me that relationships, however wonderful, are not always as permanent as the tattoos they have inspired.

One important thing to remember is to make sure the tattoo needle is double sterilized, which eliminates any concern about bacteria or infection. The process of the art itself is fairly painless for most people. The tattoo is applied with a specially made apparatus that functions somewhat like the airbrush used by painters and photographic retouchers. A high-speed needle is used to apply the tattoo, and the sensation is somewhat analogous to the feeling of a cat lightly scratching your skin. A small, rather simple design can take as little as a half hour. If you're not sure what design to choose, a skilled tattoo artist will be helpful either by sketching a possible design for you, or showing you some of the many beautiful designs that he or she has already created. So please don't be intimidated or confused if you're unable

Tattoos can be as tiny and as delicate as you like...

to decide exactly what you want. Both you and the tattoo artist can work together and collaborate on creating something with which you'll be extremely pleased.

I'd like to share with you my personal experience with the art of tattooing. A few years ago, my lover and I decided we both wanted to get the same tattoo on the same area of our bodies. Once the idea germinated in our heads, our enthusiasm grew until, like two excited children, we finally agreed upon a specific design. We made an appointment with two tattoo artists whose work we not only knew but admired and trusted as well. At this point, we could hardly wait. So when we arrived, we eagerly showed the artists our design and asked if they could apply our tattoos at the same time. They readily agreed and placed us on two couches that faced each other so we could watch each other getting our tattoos. As they were being applied, my lover and I took turns looking in each other's eyes and observing the work. It was an exhilarating, adrenaline-pounding, thrillingly intimate experience as my lover and I both felt what we were sharing. The tattoos, by the way, turned out beautifully.

Holding hands as we left, we felt extremely close and smiled almost conspiratorially at each other in the car on the way home. When we arrived, my lover scooped me up in his arms and made extremely passionate and tender love to me. Today, we still experience the love we feel by being linked together in a new and special way, and we still smile conspiratorially every time we look at the beautiful tattoos we both wear.

CHAPTER 40

TURNABOUT IS GREAT PLAY

I love to hear men speak candidly about sex, whether it be to each other, to other women or specifically to me. Not only is it enlightening, sensual, stimulating and sometimes uproariously funny, but it teaches me volumes about the male psyche—and male sexuality—in all their splendid complexity.

One of the most common characteristics usually attributed to men is their preference for a specific part of a woman's anatomy. For instance, I know many "leg men," "breast men," "face men," "inside of the thigh men," and men who worship a beautiful derriere. There are numerous rap songs that emphatically extol the virtues of a "girl's butt."

I find it humorous that we women are seldom asked about—and hardly every elaborate upon—which part of a man we are salaciously salivating over. Therefore, at the risk of sounding like a licentious iconoclast who is audaciously and single-handedly stomping onto what has formerly been male turf, I would like to share with you my discovery: that I am definitely a chest woman. That's right, and I'm hardly alone in being a cultivated connoisseur of the many pulchritudinous male assets. It just so happens that my penchant for kissing, licking, sucking and nibbling on my lover's nipples is an exciting turn-on for both of us.

How lucky I am to have a lover whose nipples are so sensitive that my lavishing attention upon them sends him into paroxysms of pure pleasure. One of my favorite and deliciously risqué things to do is to tease and tantalize and torture him by being ever so attentive to his nipples in the most public and perhaps inappropriate places. He's never sure how far I might go or exactly what I might do to implement my naughty fantasies, and I've been known to be extremely creative at business lunches, formal dinners, in line at public places, at sporting events, etc. Sometimes, all I have to do is look in his eyes, smile and then slowly let my eyes wander down to his nipples and slightly pucker my lips. Can I tell you what pleasure it gives me to watch his composure completely disintegrate as he melts like an ice cream cone on a hot summer day?

Speaking of such little pleasures, my friend Morgan offers this delightful vignette:

MORGAN

If men knew how many women talked about sex candidly and openly with their girlfriends, they would be astonished. Forget about the talk in the men's locker room. You should hear the ladies over lunch. I love our sessions together. When my girlfriend told me her lover's nipples were as sensitive as hers, it definitely got me thinking. I have a real macho lover who always wants to be in control. It was always my body that got the attention and experimentation.

Ted usually likes to end our lovemaking in the standard missionary position. While supporting himself on his arms, he can look down at me and it turns him on to see my breasts jiggling while he moves his penis in and out. Actually, I can admit that this adds tremendous visual stimulation for both of us. In this position just about the only contact we have is between his penis and my vagina. This simplifies the senses and allows me to feel every inch of him inside me. One night when I felt he was getting close to orgasm, beyond the point of no return and not likely to do anything to delay the end of his pleasure, I decided to try the nipple experiment. My arms were free and I reached up to caress his shoulders, then dragged my fingernails lightly down over his chest and then, gripping the sides of his chest with each hand, I flicked the nails of each thumb lightly over his nipples. He jerked slightly and blinked hard, almost pulling away. But the action of my fingernails seemed to further stiffen him. It felt to me like he had miraculously grown another inch or two. Hard, pure bliss. It grew and he groaned. His eyes, which were squeezed tightly shut just the moment before, blinked open and then closed again. Again he groaned. My light scratching continued side to side and occasionally circling the soft but rigid skin that encircled his nipples. He groaned when I pulled his chest closer to my mouth and sucked and licked his nipples just as he likes to do to me. I flicked one nipple between my tongue and teeth, and pulled on the other with my fingernail. He obliged with an orgasm that was far more intense than any I had seen or felt before.

He's never sure how far I might go…

Ted was always a breast man. Now we both are, with special attention to those splendidly sensitive nipples—mine and his. I couldn't wait to tell my girlfriends and share my newfound pleasure.

Thank you so much, Morgan. I'm glad I was one of the girlfriends with whom you shared this erotic adventure. Turnabout is definitely great play.

CHAPTER 41

SENSATIONAL MASTURBATION: PRACTICING FOR THE TWO OF YOU

How would you like to experience delicious, delightful guaranteed pleasure, and learn something from and about your lover at the same time? Well, in response to your resounding acquiescence and with your permission, I will attempt to elaborate and enlighten you.

What I am suggesting and encouraging you to do—with your lover—is discover the surprisingly multi-faceted, pleasurably sensational experience of mutually masturbating by watching each other at the same time, or by taking turns. There are a variety of ways to explore:

♥ One of you can watch while the other masturbates.
♥ Both of you can watch while both of you masturbate.
♥ One of you can masturbate the other while you both watch.
♥ Both of you can masturbate each other at the same time while you both watch.
♥ One of you can be blindfolded while any of the above is taking place.

♥ One of you may want to be tied up or handcuffed while any of the above is taking place.

Watching is in itself a sensational turn-on. How delightfully stimulating it is to watch your lover closely, to watch exactly how your lover does what he or she is doing. How does he please himself? Imagine how exciting it would be to see exactly how your lover likes to have it done, what secret things give him pleasure, what secret things you could do to him from now on. What does your lover experience while he's being watched, and what does your lover experience while watching you masturbate? What can you show him or her? What can you teach your lover in the ways in which your body uniquely responds? What pleasure that knowledge will give to him, what secret intimacies you'll begin to be able to share. What a lovely way to continue to discover each other more and more.

Set the mood with candles and music, or do it in the bath or a hot, steamy shower. Talk to each other and describe exactly what you're doing and what you're feeling. Then just let the waves of passion wash over you. Or you can be smolderingly silent and let the sounds of each other's pleasure speak for themselves.

Watching is in itself a sensational turn-on.

Remember, those sounds can be the most powerful turn-on and a language all their own. Sighs, whispers, moans and even the way you breathe will cascade over you and your lover in sensually delicious waves. Even when masturbating alone, the sounds of your own pleasure as you move closer to orgasm make it so much more exciting. As a matter of fact, when you masturbate without a partner, you will naturally become a better lover. Why? Because the more you're able to become aware of what stimulates you, what pleases you and the best ways in which you can receive the most pleasure, the better you're able to communicate that awareness to your lover.

Take the time to explore yourself, to really make love to yourself and to discover the mysteries deep within yourself— the hidden sources of all your secret pleasures. Only when you're able to delight in yourself can you truly convey to your lover the knowledge of what will stimulate and fulfill you.

My lover is so happy, grateful and turned on when I let him know what I like—as I am with him—and the best way to let him know is to take the time to know myself.

Well, I'm sure you know by now what your homework assignments will be for this evening. To help you with your task, I'll close this chapter with a vignette from my friend Laura:

LAURA

For a long time, I fantasized about my lover watching me masturbate. I finally worked up the courage to stop fantasizing and actually do it.

I made a point to get home early to shower and be ready when he arrived. Being ready meant that I was lying in our bed naked, propped up on a pile of pillows, the room darkened, my entire body covered with slippery body oil, just the way I like to do it when I do it to myself. I wanted Lee to see what turned me on when I turned myself on, to look and to lust. When I heard his keys in the door, I was ready. When he walked to the bedroom door and saw me, he stopped, a bit stunned at first. His eyes went from my eyes to my hands and back to my eyes. By now, he had a sly grin on his face and dropped the packages he was carrying. As I continued my sliding and squeezing and probing, he also dropped his clothes on the floor. Then he came and sat down on the bed next to me. Watching everything closely, he asked me why I did this thing and that thing. I told him in extremely graphic detail. Needless to say, I had his total attention.

Soon, he was touching himself in the same way I was touching myself, rubbing some of the oil from my body onto his hands. Then he picked up my rhythm, just the way he wanted it. Our eyes were locked. He brought himself to the edge, I brought myself to the edge— then we crossed the edge together.

What a lovely and mutually satisfying way for you and your lover to discover and learn about each other.

CHAPTER 42

THE BIG
TEASE

I'm sure you're all aware by now that sexual teasing done in a provocatively sensual and creative way is one of my favorite things. With just a bit of ingenuity, I totally believe it can be elevated to an absolute art form.

For instance, there is no reason you can't play your lover like a Stradivarius. Or you can turn him into an Olympic athlete as he tries to overpower you with his stamina. Or you can turn your lover into a grandmaster of unexpected moves as you both skillfully maneuver each other around your intricate sexual chessboard. Sharpening your fencing skills as you seductively thrust and parry with your lover will always inflame the libido.

There are an infinite variety of ways for you and your lover to intermittently torture and dazzle each other with absolutely sinful, sexual suspense. The thing I like best about the suspense is never knowing which roles my lover and I will assume at any given moment. I love the excitement and spontaneity of feeling as if I were participating in a beautifully orchestrated sensual ballet. Sometimes I simply love the way my lover is able to make me quiver like a tuning fork when I have no choice but to surrender to his expertise.

And by the way, no choice can be a great choice, as demonstrated by my friend Liz and her sizzling story.

LIZ

Jimmy is a great lover. He laughs a lot. He never gets too serious about it. And he loves to tease.

I never know what kind of night it's going to be. He always takes his time doing the things he knows really turn me on. Love bites under my arm, on the back of my neck, all around my shoulder blades, working his way down my back to the cheeks of my butt. A nip here, a nip there, slowly, with no rush. While his mouth is moving, his fingers are moving as well. All over me, skipping around my body, outlining the edges of my fingers, my nose, my lips, my chin and down my throat, scratching the palms of my hands, always moving.

His tongue is like a slippery little eel, usually following the place his fingers have just visited. Alternately flicking and licking, always teasing, always tantalizing. Absolutely no penetration of any kind. When I'm frantic almost beyond hope, he finally enters me, or semi-enters me. At this point, I can hardly stand the frustration, but he just smiles down at me, barely moving his hips except when I move toward him. Every time I do, he slides those hips away, somehow keeping his penis only one inch deep, or he just takes it out completely. I'll do anything to get it now, but no matter how much I beg, he won't acquiesce. His grin just gets wider and wider and his eyes get narrower. The first time Jimmy gave me the one-inch treatment, I naturally assumed it was part of the build-up and that eventually he would plunge deep into me, satisfying all the pent-up frustration and tension— but he didn't! He just continued his one-inch tease.

His tongue is like a slippery little eel...

When he knows I finally just can't hold back any longer, when I can't take it anymore, he takes his penis in his hands and slides it up and down through the well-lubricated lips of my labia, and up and over and all around my clitoris, while I explode in waves of pleasure. I'm so grateful to Jimmy for showing me that one inch can be the most powerful measurement I've ever experienced.

When Liz first related this story, I couldn't wait to find out how long my lover and I could hold out, experiencing the wonder of a one-inch penetration. Isn't it wonderful to be able to conduct exciting erotic experiments and to learn something new every day? Thank you, Liz and Jimmy.

CHAPTER 43

DIRTY DANCING

When I was a teenager, going to a weekend dance with my girlfriends was one of the most exciting things in the world. Together, we'd spend the entire week discussing it, planning what we would wear, who we would see and what boys we hoped would ask us to dance.

And actually getting to dance with the dreamy boys, on whom we had enormous crushes, made our teenage dreams totally come true.

When the evening began, my girlfriends and I always made sure to dance as provocatively as we could in front of the boys, employing all the moves we had practiced at each other's houses and in front of our mirrors at home. We did our best to incite their libidos, which was hardly a difficult task, considering what horny puppies they were. As the evening unfolded, both the boys and girls became more bold and started dancing with each other; that's when the night really began to sizzle.

When a slow song came on, my girlfriends and I would smile as we passed each other on the dance floor, snuggled tightly in our boyfriends' arms.

The feeling was romantic and exciting and thrillingly

sensual as our bodies touched and pressed against each other. I remember wanting the song to play forever because the feeling of being so closely intertwined with a beautiful boy was the ultimate thrill.

And what made it so thrilling was that, although it was safe, it was soooo sexy. We could bump and grind and touch and feel and slide and rub and writhe and gyrate and tease and torture each other to the point of madness and delirium. With the music pounding in our ears, working us up to a fever pitch, I'm surprised we didn't all rip each other's clothes off right there on the dance floor!

The delightful thing about these memories is that my lover and I thoroughly enjoy re-creating them, and they seem almost better the second time around. We've found so many tantalizing ways to dance ourselves into a frenzy of passion that, depending on the moment, the place and our mood, we range all the way from soft, subtle sensuality to the boldest of dynamic and explosive displays.

The wonderful thing about the overwhelming variety of both music and dance is that within their vast expanse is contained every possible means of expression. Moving from sensual slow dancing to the smoldering tango, to the bump and grind of pumping hard rock, all the way to the blistering hot lambada, constitutes a truly movable feast.

...I'm surprised we didn't all rip each other's clothes off right there on the dance floor!

Not only does dancing implement the realization of the most delectable sexual fantasies, but it also completely disintegrates sexual tensions, hang-ups, misgivings and inhibitions. It's the most delightfully pleasurable therapy around.

So deny yourselves no longer! Get out

on that dance floor with your lover, let the music surround you, free yourselves from constraint, explore and discover every inch of each other's body, feel the beat, the pulse and the heat—and simply lose yourself in the moment.

While you're thinking about that wonderful feeling of abandon, I'll end this chapter by sharing with you the experience of my friend Monique:

MONIQUE

In Paris, there are many wonderful places to go dancing. Clubs on top of tall buildings, clubs in caves and really sexy places like Jimmy Z's, Regine's and Banduche. What is wonderful about all these dance clubs and discos is the wonderful things that Roger and I do to each other while we're dancing. I love to wear tight tops tucked into loose-fitting jeans or pants with large pockets. All the while we're dancing, Roger is caressing and touching and bumping my body. I love it when he dances up close behind me, pushing his penis against my butt, sliding his hands into my pockets and the front of my slacks. Then his fingers go to work. He gently, and sometimes not so gently, pulls my pubic hairs and presses his fingertips against my vagina and down over the covering of my clitoris. What a sensation. And all to the rhythm of the rock or disco music pounding through our ears into the center of our bodies.

We can do this for hours, both our bodies hot and shiny with sweat, as we dance slowly and then furiously and then slowly again. Roger's fingers reach out and pinch me here, then there, each time making my nipples swell a bit larger and harder. I love it when he puts his leg between my legs and literally picks me up off the floor, with the hardness of his thigh and knee being gripped by my thigh.

The more crowded the dance floor, the better we like it. Bumping and sliding and sliding and bumping. Also, the more people pressing against each other and against us, the more difficult it is for anyone to catch us at our secret, sexy dancing. It's also fun when I slide or bump my hand across the sweet part of someone else's lover who's dancing close to Roger and me. Those guys never know if it's just an accident or if something is going on. A dangerous game of mine, perhaps, but I love it, and Roger doesn't mind.

I'm not sure if every man is as generous as Roger—unless, of course, Roger is so busy doing the same thing as Monique that he doesn't notice.

CHAPTER 44

SMOOTH OPERATOR

A few years ago, a most beautiful singer named Sade recorded a song entitled "Smooth Operator." The song was extremely popular not only because it was sultry and sensuous, but also because the subject matter was something to which so many women could relate. And even though there is an ambivalence attached to the term itself, there's no denying the attraction of a man who knows how to seduce a woman artfully and well. Perhaps the term implies a bit of slickness or duplicity, but it also implies a certain finesse with which a man navigates in order to pursue and attain a woman's attentions.

As I thought about the concept, I began to wonder how much longer the term *smooth operator* would seem to apply exclusively to a man, and when women would begin to take the initiative to be thought of in those terms. I personally have no compunctions about taking the initiative with a man in whom I am interested, because I am not afraid of going after what I want. But I've certainly not always been this confident or self-possessed and have, in the past, simply waited for the man to make the first move.

Luckily, that phase didn't last too long because, number

one, I don't seem to possess an over-abundance of patience, and number two, it seemed rather silly for me to sit and wait for someone else to make the moves I was perfectly capable of making myself in order to get what I want.

Now I know I'm not the only one who feels this way, but those of us who do are in the minority because, unfortunately, women and men have, for centuries, been conditioned to believe that, in terms of pursuit, men are the aggressors and women are to remain passive. That approach is not only archaic, illogical and impractical, but it's also something that both men and women want very much to change. How do I know this? Because I've spoken candidly with a tremendous number of people of both sexes who are fed up with the expectations, responsibilities and constraints imposed by such restrictive behavior patterns. There are so many women to whom I have spoken who would love to, at times, assume the role of an aggressive, smoldering temptress without appearing pushy and overbearing. And an equal number of men would simply love to experience the luxury of being wooed, pursued and swept off their feet by a woman who knows what she wants, and how to get it.

So the time is ripe for all of you women to take the initiative, make those moves you've always wanted to make and play out those fantasies in which you totally take charge! Remember, as with anything else, practice makes perfect; the more you do it, the easier and more fun it becomes. And in addition to the enjoyment both you and your lover will derive, women will have the added pleasure of their man's undying gratitude for relieving him of the relentless burden of always having to be the initiator. So "How do I seduce thee? Let me count the ways." Here are a few suggestions. Let's begin with Beth:

BETH

Sometimes when I'm hot and Bob's not, I like to get a bit naughty. Like standing in front of him, stripping off my T-shirt, squeezing my breasts, teasing my nipples and running my tongue all over my lips. All the while looking Bob right in the eye. This does tend to get his attention. So does zipping my jeans open and wiggling a hand down into my panties...

Next we have Jill:

JILL

When I'm ready for sex but don't want to hit Charlie over the head with it, I invite him to a shower for two. Once under the water, I take things in hand, and I don't mean the soap...

Next we have Elaine:

ELAINE

Scott loves massages, so it's easy to initiate sex between the two of us. I simply start with his head and work my way down, using body oil all over his shoulders, nipples, belly and genitals. It doesn't take too long before I'm on the receiving end...

Next we hear from Patty:

PATTY

There are times, especially Friday nights, when Jerry comes home so frazzled that I can tell he just doesn't have the energy for making any decisions about going out. Oh, he's ready for anything, just as long as he doesn't have to set it up. So I make it easy for him. I invite him out. I plan the date, book the dinner reservation, get the game tickets, whatever. I also reserve a hotel room and pick up the keys the afternoon before our "date." Then when the festivities are over, we go back to my place—the hotel room—where I put the

...men would simply love to experience the luxury of being wooed...

*moves on Jerry. There are times when he truly enjoys and appreci-
ates not making the decisions. And I love making it easy for him
not to have to.*

One of my own favorite ways to take the initiative is to stop
in the middle of a battle of words with my lover and simply
do the unexpected, especially when he's in mid-sentence,
being very adamant about expressing his point of view. What
I do is walk over to him, put my arms around him, look him
straight in the eye and say, "Oh, yeah? Well, here's what I
have to say about that!" and plant a great big juicy kiss right
on his beautiful, sexy mouth.

After his initial surprise, we usually engage in a bit of
friendly wrestling, which inevitably turns into red-hot lovemaking. And while we're on the subject of initiating sex, I'd
like to share with you the expertise of my friend Angela:

ANGELA

*The first time I ever really enjoyed being the total aggressor was the
first time I was out with Peter. We had met at a party a couple of
days before, and he asked me to have dinner at the beach. En route
to the restaurant, we talked and we laughed. He had only given me
a little kiss at my front door, but I was already interested and
already turned on. At the restaurant, we had a lovely dinner and a
few bottles of wine. Peter held my hand to emphasize a story he was
telling, and an electric shock went through me. After the restaurant,
we continued our animated conversation during the ride home,
which began to be punctuated by touches, caresses and all those
things embryonic lovers do to take the next steps in their own secret
sexual rituals. At one point, when I was leaning quite close to him,
my earring fell off and landed on the floor in front of the driver's
seat, so I reached down between his legs to retrieve it. When I discovered how excited he was by my hand brushing against his taut
penis, straining to be set free, I just couldn't help myself. I rubbed it
through the gabardine and then opened the zipper. Peter gasped, but
kept on driving. I took his organ in my hand and kissed it up and*

down with my lips. I licked it with my tongue and gently lowered my mouth around his wonderful, warm weapon. Since he had to pay attention to his driving, I had the control. I was careful not to be too aggressive or to do anything too surprising; it was just gentle foreplay. When we pulled into my garage, he turned to me and spread my legs and slowly but surely entered me. We talk about that night often. While we don't recommend this as something you might want to try since it can be extremely distracting, it was heavenly for us. Every time I ride with Peter, my hand always rests in that special place. Just so he won't forget.

As if he ever could! Remember how exciting and rewarding it is for a woman to take the initiative in creating those magical memories with her lover.

CHAPTER 45

THE ULTIMATE WORKOUT

Sometimes I love going to the gym to work out, sometimes I'm ambivalent and sometimes I downright loathe it and have to literally grit my teeth and practically drag myself there kicking and screaming. But no matter what my mood or degree of initial reluctance, after finally getting into my workout, I invariably begin to start feeling better and always end up glad I came. Granted, I know a lot of my sense of well-being is due to ridding myself of a great deal of tension and stress, also the wonderful release of my friendly endorphins, and all the wonderful benefits my body has derived from the exercise, but in all honesty, I must confess there is another crucial element that contributes to my feeling of euphoria. And what, you ask, is that crucial element? Well, it's simply the admiring looks I get from and give to all the beautiful males I encounter, huffing and puffing their way into fitness heaven. What infinite wisdom, I ask myself, propelled me into making the extremely fortuitous decision of joining a co-ed gym?

As I gaze longingly at the bulging biceps of the man on the machine next to mine, a voice whispers softly into my brain, "Who cares why you joined? What matters is that you did."

So I continue to admire the pulchritude.

Now, I take my workout quite seriously and don't allow myself to become distracted. But like most people, I'm perfectly capable of doing two things at the same time; so I make the effort to do them both to the best of my ability.

There have also been times when I have looked and felt totally grungy and didn't want to even acknowledge the existence of the male of the species as I sweated and strained. I remember on one occasion looking in the mirror, after having worked myself into total exhaustion, and making eye contact with a handsome man. I was completely taken aback when I realized he was gazing at me with an extremely flirtatious look in his eyes. How could this be? I thought, as the sweat streamed down my face. At that moment, I learned the extremely valuable lesson that a woman not only doesn't have to be at her best and most beautiful to be appealing to a man, but ironically, she's sometimes most attractive when she's simply relaxed and not at all aware of how she appears. That revelation was so simple and so clear that I began to laugh and, of course, so did he.

Needless to say, our laughter was a perfect icebreaker, which led to not only a conversation but a friendship as well.

Remember, visual delights are meant to be shared equally by both men and women at a co-ed gym.

For an excellent example from the male perspective, Lorenzo offers his bodybuilding experience:

...he was gazing at me with an extremely flirtatious look in his eyes.

LORENZO
The first time I noticed Sheila was when she passed me at the Sports Connection. What a piece of work! I've never seen a butt move like she made it move; tight, well-muscled buttocks that swayed as she looked like

she was walking on eggs. She had small but high breasts whose nipples brushed against her flimsy bodysuit. I smiled. She smiled. Great beginning! Then she threw herself into working on all the machines that were usually a man's domain. And she wasn't bad at it. I noticed how her hair stuck to her face with the exertion. I noticed how her shoulders and arms and thighs were beaded with sweat. I noticed how great she looked without makeup. I never thought muscles on a woman were sexy before, but they definitely were on Sheila. I was totally disarmed.

When she was taking a break, I offered to show her a couple things on the machines that would provide quicker results with less energy. So we worked out several times together—with nothing more than a handshake and a quick kiss on the cheek. I knew she was special and I was prepared to take my time.

Finally, she suggested that we spend time together outside the gym. But I still waited. I held her hand, I hugged her a little, I brushed her cheek. But I never pushed it. I wanted her to want me with the same determination she used on her workouts. Luckily, I had some exercise equipment at home, so, of course, I invited her over for some private instruction. It's easy to have a lot of body contact when you're exercising together, and I tried hard to conceal my excitement. When we finally came together, it was as though a moment in time had been fixed for that purpose. I don't quite remember what triggered it, but there we were, rolling around the floor, two hot, sweaty bodies that had already taken on the flavor of each other simply by proximity. Finally I did what I had wanted to do for so long—I tore her leotard in half and exposed the hard little breasts. In my greediness, I pushed them together and tried to get them both in my mouth. She straddled me and the muscles in her thighs stood out from her knees to her groin. Her vagina dripped with sweat and excitement. She reached down and bit me, moaning. We were two lithe animals in the throes of uninhibited passion stoked by weeks of stalking and lying in wait.

Since that time some six months ago, we've made love in many different ways, in many different moods, in many different moments. But my exercise room still has a special fascination for us. We've

discovered the ultimate exercise after we've used up everything else.
The calories melt with our generated heat. Sheila's body never looks
so good as when it's covered with sweat, or covered with me.

Lorenzo, we love your expertise, as well as your appetite.

Well, it's clear that a workout can definitely lead to getting worked up. And gaining strength will most certainly
lead to more endurance (how much do we love that?). And
if that's not enough, just think of the endless possibilities
that open up when one's body is more fluid, more supple,
more resilient...

CHAPTER 46

EROTIC PHOTOGRAPHY

W e've all heard the expression "A picture is worth a thousand words." Well, that's often only the beginning. A photograph can be so powerful that it evokes a multiplicity of responses, and an erotic photo can awaken any dormant libido.

Through the magic of still photography, lovers can create the most incredible heat and passion with each other by playing photographer and model and, if they like, switching roles. The best thing about it is that there are no rules, no constraints, and the only boundaries are the ones that are self-imposed.

What fun it is to pretend you're Helmut Newton, David Chan (the gentleman who photographs the Girls of "wherever" for *Playboy*), Francis Giacobetti, Herb Ritts or any number of famous photographers, or you can create your own erotic masterpieces by using a trusty, reliable, instantly gratifying Polaroid camera.

Try varying the lighting, the positions and the wardrobe, or use body paint to create a totally unique and smoldering look. Pretend you're shooting a "Victoria's Secret" or "Night Classics" catalogue. Not only can you use lingerie that's beautiful and provocative, but emulating the way the models pose creates a body language that's impossible to resist.

If you'd like to surprise your lover by giving him a special, romantic or simply erotic gift for a special occasion, or for no particular occasion whatsoever, try going to a professional photographer who specializes in romantic "boudoir" photography.

Through the use of exotic surroundings, flattering lighting and the photographer's expertise, you can become your lover's own personal centerfold, complete with red-hot sexy poses, in and out of extremely intimate apparel.

Men can also surprise and delight their lovers by giving them professional photos shot either in the nude or sexily and suggestively clad. Pretending to be a Chippendale's dancer can create erotically charged, interesting and sometimes hilarious photographs. Remember, although photos of your lover are wonderful to share, it can be an enormously erotic experience to carry some of the photos with you when you're separated by time or distance. One look and you're instantly infused with longing for your lover—and that, of course, makes your return that much more meaningful.

And if you lover has, without your knowledge, placed an erotic photo of himself or herself in a pocket or briefcase for you to discover while you're away, the pleasure of discovery is sweet and stimulating. An added bonus is that it builds a level of anticipation so great that it becomes an erotic tidal wave that will engulf both of you the moment you see each other.

So if you'll excuse me, I have an appointment with a professional photographer that I absolutely can't miss, and I also think I'd better put a rush on the

The best thing about it is that there are no rules...

development of the photos so that I can slip one into my lover's pocket, in his medicine cabinet, his underwear drawer, his glove compartment...

While I'm gone, here are Mark's and Kristen's sojourns into the world of erotic photography for your reading pleasure:

MARK

Kristen always wanted to be a photographer's model but never was. Now she is. And I'm the photographer. Kristen never wanted to be a photographer, but now she is that too—with me as the model. How do we do it? All with the help of Polaroids. Talk about instant gratification.

Some nights we'll shoot dozens of pictures of each other. Partly clothed, clothed not at all, partly sexy, partly dirty, very dirty, erect, tumescent, dripping, whatever turns us on as our sensual photo session goes on. And on. Full-body shots. Both-body shots. Close-ups. Some so close that they're practically inside us. Very wet and wonderful to look at over and over again.

Kristen and I keep our Polaroids in a kind of private library where they're handy for sharing past moments that help generate the heat for our next lovemaking. And believe me, it gets so hot, we practically ignite.

Considering all the film we've bought, it's a shame we don't have stock in Polaroid.

KRISTEN

I love to stretch and arch and twist for the camera when Mark is taking our private pictures. I love to study the photographs in Playboy *and reenact them or interpret them, pulling my panties down and arching my butt into the air, or pulling my bra down so my breasts are exposed and my nipples get hard. I love to roll around and stick my butt in the direction of the camera when I hear Mark's excited cries of encouragement and approval. He doesn't know it, but I practice this in front of a mirror when I'm alone. So he thinks I'm just a naturally great model. It gets me so hot to see him getting hot. I fantasized posing for strange men in this manner with the thought in my mind that I'm gorgeous and nasty. But posing in privacy gives you complete license to rub your body for the camera, to grab your breasts, to fondle your clitoris. One time I was posing in an extremely provocative way with my legs spread wide. Mark moved in for a close-up and got so excited that after snapping the photo, he threw the camera on the ground, grabbed me and started licking my clitoris, saying he couldn't wait another second. Whenever we look at that photo, we always remember what happened afterward.*

Too bad they don't have any photos of that! Well, there's always the next time!

CHAPTER 47

ALMOST A
MENAGE À TROIS

T he scenario in this highly erotic chapter works well
only if both you and your lover are very much aware
and respectful of each other's sexual boundaries and
limits. And because it involves a third person, pleasure can
quickly turn into pain if these boundaries are crossed. With
that in mind, I will elaborate. The almost menage consists of
you, your lover and a third person who participates only in
the foreplay. This experience is probably orchestrated most
easily by lovers who live in big cities, which are more conducive to anonymity. Meetings at a hotel will ensure no
intrusions or interruptions.

In a large city, you can hire an "escort" or "model" to join
you for an hour or as long as you wish and can afford. During
that time, your escort can be asked to dance for you, do a
sexy strip tease, massage you and your lover, oil your bodies,
help you undress your lover, light candles or pour champagne, or whatever it is you think creates a sexy, erotic and
safer setting for a menage à trois.

Safer is the key word. The third person is not allowed to
participate in any penetration or other activities involving
potentially unsafe sex. But that still leaves a wide variety of

sensual playacting. And when you and your lover are ready to become intimate, the third person makes a discreet exit.

If the following true confession from Suzanne is too risqué for you and your lover, then enjoy it as a fantasy. If not, then consider it a possible suggestion.

SUZANNE

I have always turned down any threesome invitations from previous boyfriends because I never quite trusted how I would feel in the middle of it. When you're all groping and grabbing and at that point of no return, what is the sexual etiquette if you decide it's not your cup of tea and you want to keep the relationship strictly à deux? It's a great fantasy turn-on, but to actually do it? And what about those feelings of jealousy which I was so sure would come up if my man was making love to another woman right there in front of me?

Peter, my longtime lover and helpmate, had asked me several times to invite a female friend to join in with us, but I had always demurred. With his birthday coming up, however, I was discussing this recurring fantasy with an old and enlightened friend of mine, Crystal, who admitted she had indulged in a few threesomes herself. I told her that if I were ever going to experience this with anyone, it would be her. But in the next breath, I told her I could never handle the idea of watching Peter make love to someone else. It was then that Crystal came up with the idea of an "almost menage" as a birthday present for Peter. She would come as a masseuse to give him a birthday gift massage, with me assisting. She would help contribute to his and my arousal, but would leave at the right moment, before things got out of hand. What a sensational idea! Peter had never met Crystal. This was going to be interesting.

...he groaned again to the feeling of four hands on his body.

After an incredible birthday dinner I had cooked for Peter and several heady glasses of wine, Crystal arrived. I had told Peter that his birthday gift from me was going to be the massage experience of his life. Crystal's masseuse uniform was "white and tight," a combination of short shorts, a T-shirt and knee socks. One look almost knocked Peter's socks off. He was ready for a massage immediately, and went into the bedroom to strip and wrap a towel around his hips. When he returned, the lights were turned down, the music was up and the air was heavy with the smell of the musky oil Crystal had brought with her. He groaned a sigh of pleasure as she began to massage his shoulders, neck and back with the oil. When I joined in, he groaned again to the feeling of four hands on his body. I loved the feeling of Crystal's hands intermixing with mine and the smell of the oil on Peter's hard and sexy body.

When I rubbed the oil in the crease of his beautiful butt, he finally raised his head to look around. At that moment, I leaned across the table and kissed Crystal. We both watched him, keeping both our hands squeezing his cheeks and legs as we held our kiss. Crystal pulled away slightly as Peter turned over. In one quick movement, she pulled off her white T-shirt, exposing her breasts to Peter's grasp. She squirted oil onto his hands and fingers and all over her upper body. His hands were all over her breasts and neck and shoulders. I pulled open Peter's towel and squirted the oil all over his thighs and penis. While I massaged him there, I kissed him deeply and passionately. Crystal and I continued our now highly erotic massage. We had Peter's full attention, and as we massaged him, his hands played with our bodies. He was in heaven!

Finally, I went on my knees to take Peter into my mouth to bring him completely into my experience alone. He closed his eyes, lifted his hips and put his hands on my head to guide me. At that point, I had him completely.

Crystal sensed that the time had come to go. And she did, silently and discreetly. I was happy it was just Peter and me, alone, and he told me it was his best birthday ever. Honestly, the introduction of another person into just the foreplay made it a truly erotic evening for both of us.

Once again, although this evening was staged for a man, it works equally well for a woman. On a birthday or special day for her, a male lover and another man can provide the same kind of pleasurable foreplay—with the same kind of disappearing act at the right time. And remember, the right time is different for everyone. Indulge yourselves with a third person only as far as it's comfortable for both of you and not intrusive upon the intimacy you reserve only for each other.

CHAPTER 48

TIE ME UP, TIE ME DOWN

The idea of being overpowered and swept away by someone as heartbreakingly sexy as Antonio Banderas is practically every woman's fantasy. In the film *Tie Me Up! Tie Me Down!*, Antonio kidnaps a woman with whom he is desperately in love, but she, unfortunately, doesn't know he exists. To make her fall in love with him in return, he takes her to a secret love-nest where he can have his exclusive and uninterrupted way with her.

Tying her to a bed, he proceeds, over a period of time, to stimulate, arouse, deny, tease and eventually captivate her into turning from a most unwilling to a totally adoring and submissive love-slave. This is done without physically harming her in any way, because his goal was not to hurt her, but to make her fall in love with him—which she eventually did.

Now believe it or not, this is a fantasy in which you and your partner can very safely and easily indulge. In fact, I guarantee you that you can easily have your cake and thoroughly enjoy it too.

The only thing I ask is that you and your lover don't indulge in this fantasy until you both feel you have developed the level of intimacy and mutual respect that will engender total trust. Trust that will allow you to completely enjoy this risqué role-playing.

One of the most exciting aspects of one partner being totally dominant and the other submissive is that the situations and circumstances can be as diverse as your imaginations can encompass, and the roles can be unpredictably and surprisingly reversed!

What I like best about this deliciously naughty sexual game is that whatever role either you or your lover assumes, whether it be the dominant or submissive partner, both are equally erotically charged and equally fun to play. And in the secret language that only you and you lover share, depending on the moment, you spontaneously decide who overwhelms whom and who gets to unquestionably overpower their ostensibly resistant victim and ultimately melt their resistance through the sheer power of his or her incredible sexual prowess and skill.

And if that's not enough, the submissive partner literally begs to be completely and totally ravaged beyond his or her wildest dreams. But only after he or she has left no stone unturned to fight, struggle, twist, turn and resist in a valiant but ultimately futile attempt to deny the inevitable.

For a totally erotically charged and creative version of this scenario, Joni shares her vignette.

JONI

My breathing became heavy as my excitement continued to increase.

Sometimes my boyfriend James decides that the time is just right for us to play the game of dominance and submission. One night when I came home from work he was waiting just inside the door holding a pair of handcuffs.

Motioning for me to go into the living room, he told me I wasn't allowed to speak, but had to stand very still and not move. He then put a scarf over my mouth and tied it in the back of my head. After quickly removing my clothing, he handcuffed my hands behind my back and put a clamp on each of my nipples and made me sit on the couch with my knees up and my legs completely spread. Then he sat across from me just savoring my position.

After devouring me with his eyes, he picked up his Polaroid camera and took a few photos of me in that pose. He then repositioned me in a few other submissive positions, including being on my knees and one with my bottom right toward the camera, prominently displayed. He then made me get on my knees again, pulled the scarf out of my mouth, took his erect penis out of his slacks and ordered me to suck it. Just as he was about to have an orgasm, he made me stop and told me we were going upstairs.

In the bedroom he took off my handcuffs and ordered me to lie on the bed while he tied my arms and legs to the four posters.

He picked up a riding crop and began to stroke my neck, my nipples, my stomach, my vagina, my clitoris, my anus, my thighs and legs and down to my toes. As he tapped me lightly on my thighs, I began to twist and writhe in my restraints. My breathing became heavy as my excitement continued to increase. Knowing that he would never hurt me, I moaned from sheer pleasure and anticipation. He alternated stroking me with a riding crop and a tasseled silk cord till I thought I couldn't stand it for one more second. Suddenly, I felt his hot lips on my vagina, his tongue working my clitoris. Slowly he slid one and then two fingers in my anus and massaged me until I literally exploded in his mouth, completely losing every bit of control over my body.

James quickly removed his clothing, ripped the scarf off my face and put his beautifully throbbing penis in my mouth again. In a frenzy, I licked and sucked until I thought he would explode. But he pulled out again and reached down to my nipples, tightening the clamps just ever so slightly.

Picking up the riding crop again, Jimmy undid the ties of my feet, turned me onto my side, and lightly spanked my bottom. He then commanded me to lie on my back, spread my legs as far as I could and beg him to fuck me, which I quickly and eagerly did. He slowly started to penetrate me, then pulled out and made me beg him again!

This time, I practically screamed as I begged him to enter me again. Jimmy readily complied and began thrusting into me until we both practically collapsed from the intensity of our orgasm. Ever since that night, I can hardly wait for Jimmy to be waiting by my door (with his handcuffs, of course).

Thank you, Joni! After reading your vignette, I can hardly wait to get home to my lover and our own four-poster bed.

CHAPTER 49

TANTRA—UNLEASHING YOUR SEXUAL POWER

Tantra is a mystical experience of joy in which sex is energizing, sex is life-giving, sex is holy. It is the ability, through the union of two human beings, to discover the divine. It is a religion in which one achieves a feeling of ecstasy, a state of pure bliss.

Wait a minute! Slow down! Is something like this even humanly possible? And if it is, is it something that even I can experience? And if even a lowly, unevolved being like myself could possibly experience such an exalted state, would it entail a lifetime of meditation, study and contemplation to achieve? And do I really want to get involved in all this exalted sexual bliss? Isn't it way over my humble head? And doesn't it sound like a lot of work?

These were only a few of the many questions that ran through my mind at the overwhelming prospect of this much heightened awareness. But I was mesmerized by the magnetic pull and beckoned by the almost hypnotic realm of possibility implicit in these concepts.

When I first discovered Tantra, I was at a point in my life where I was questioning not only myself but everything around me—virtually all of existence. I wanted something more, something greater than myself. My search took me in a multiplicity of directions in which clarity and illusion became intertwined to the degree that any understanding became more and more fragmented and obscure. My biggest obstacle was the wall of fear and mistrust I had created around myself which was completely retrograde to the achievement of any possible awareness.

Then one day that wall became one of my greatest teachers, because in walking through it, I evolved from being its servant to becoming its master. Initially, the fear with which I battled most was that of intimacy, and the road I traveled to walk through that fear led me to the mystical path of Tantra. In my search to understand the beauty and complexity of Tantra, I walked through a doorway into a world in which my life would be forever changed.

At this point you're probably thinking, "What the hell is she talking about?" So at the risk of sounding like I'm getting ready to float down the river of enlightenment into the great void, I'd like to attempt to scratch the surface of a subject that would take at least a volume to explain.

Tantra is a religion, an ancient Eastern science born in India around 5000 B.C. through the cult of the Hindu god Shiva and his consort, the goddess Shakti. Shiva was the embodiment of pure energy. It is a belief system that embraces sexuality as a doorway to ecstasy and enlightenment. And although that premise seems deceptively simplistic, Tantra is so endlessly multi-faceted that it becomes more and more beautiful as it continues to unfold and disclose its exquisite secrets.

In her book *The Art of Sexual Ecstasy*, Margo Anand explains that the Hindus believed that Shiva united spiritually and sexually with Shakti, giving form to his spirit and thus creating the universe. Tantra, therefore, views the creation of the universe as an erotic act of love. She states that Tantra was also a rebellion against the moralistic Brahmins, who believed that sexuality had to be denied in order to

attain enlightenment. On the contrary, Tantra accepts everything and feels that all experience is a learning process, an
opportunity for self-awareness and growth.

Tantra embraces opposites as part of a whole. The concepts of male and female are two polarities that merge in
every human being. And when that union of two beings
takes place, a new dimension is experienced, that of the
Sacred. Within that sacredness of sexual unity is the connection to the Life Force, the source of creation. So Tantra
teaches us that the raw energy of the sex drive can be transformed into pure ecstasy. As I continued to learn the teach-
ings of Tantra, I eventually discovered that this seemingly
phenomenal concept is actually true. I learned that orgasm
could be transformed into an ecstatic vibration that spreads
through the entire body and creates an energy that could
revitalize, heal and ultimately lead to a state of bliss.

State of bliss? If at this point you're wondering if I've gone
off the deep end, please don't worry. I assure you that Tantra
also offers detailed and easy-to-understand instructions on
how to achieve all this pleasure with your partner and also
within yourself. And speaking of easy-to-understand instructions, I'd like to give you an example of the wonderful possibilities of Tantra. Perhaps you've heard about the super-
human sexual abilities of one of our most talented rock
singers, Sting. When asked by Jay Leno on the *Tonight Show*
whether it's true that he was able to have sex for four contin-
uous hours, he humbly replied yes. Completely taken aback,
Jay quickly asked Sting's wife, Trudy, if that were indeed the
case. Without a second of hesitation, Trudy shook her head
most emphatically and shot back the word *seven* with the
expression of a woman who couldn't have been happier or
more fulfilled. Needless to say, at that point, Jay was speech-
less as Sting smiled and stated simply that he practiced yoga.

Upon that modest disclosure, the question that came to
everyone's mind was, of course, "How in the hell does he do
it?" Well, I assure you that it can be done—if you're willing

to do a bit of research by learning specific yogic techniques from a qualified teacher and reading certain books on yoga such as *Sexual Energy and Yoga* by Elizabeth Haich. This is also the area in which Tantra comes in handy because in books such as Margo Anand's, the techniques necessary to prolong orgasm as well as heighten and lengthen the whole sexual experience are very well explained. Now if this sounds as though it entails a great deal of effort, please remember the incredible prowess of Sting and just imagine being able to have the same experience with your own lover. The wonderful thing is that you can! And I wish you all the pleasure your bodies can encompass and contain.

On a more spiritual level, Tantra teaches how to achieve a balance, stating that the external and the internal are but movements of the same energy, and that both men and women have a dominant and recessive polarity. In other words, men have female hormones and women have male hormones, which enables both sexes to experience the opposite sides of their nature within themselves. Unfortunately, due mostly to societal constraints and social stigma, this ability has, for both men and women, remained for the most part dormant. Even Jung stressed the importance of men allowing themselves to recognize the anima (female element) and women the animus (male element) within themselves. In Tantra, those restrictive boundaries are transcended and these polarities are integrated to achieve a state of oneness, which is called Ecstatic Awareness.

In more practical terms, the fewer the boundaries, the greater the possibility for both you and your lover to break out of

...the raw energy of the sex drive can be transformed...

restrictive and outdated gender roles. And within that new freedom, you will discover the opportunity and, of course, the thrill of experiencing the most unforgettable sex that ever existed.

And now I'd like to share with you an experience so unforgettable that it changed my life forever.

Many years ago, my husband, who was far more experienced than I in every way, taught me to expand my awareness of many Eastern religions and philosophies, including Tantra. At first I was very intimidated by Tantra, but John was extremely gentle and patient and was a master in the art of lovemaking.

One evening when I arrived home, I found the house filled with candles and incense. I was enveloped by a myriad of scents and fragrances and surrounded by soft music as John led me into the bedroom, where it seemed as though hundreds of tiny candles flickered in mirrored reflections of themselves.

As he guided me toward the bed, I could only gaze in wonderment as I saw what seemed like thousands of multicolored rose petals completely covering the bed and engulfing me with their perfumed beauty.

Transfixed, I felt as though I were in a dream, every sensation being heightened as he slowly undressed me and began massaging my body with a warm, smooth, slippery oil. Removing his clothing, he guided me onto the bed, where we rolled slowly in the soft flowers, covering each other with petals and oil. Then he started kissing me with long, luscious kisses, as only he could do, all over my face and body, always coming back to gaze into my eyes, always staying connected.

Whispering softly, he asked me not to close my eyes but to lock into his as the intensity grew. I felt his hand slide down my body right to my clitoris. He smiled as my body began to quiver, his fingers working their silky magic, my breathing becoming more and more intense. Writhing under his expert and seamless touch, waves of pleasure began to wash over me as I started to tense, knowing I was coming closer and closer to orgasm. All of sudden he stopped, put his finger just under my vagina and slowly pressed that tiny area of my pulsating body.

Puzzled, I searched his eyes for what to do next. Slowly, he put the fingers of his other hand on my tailbone, pressing lightly, and started moving his fingers up the small of my back, exerting a very light pressure. Still locked into my gaze, he started rubbing my wet, dripping, expectant clitoris again and whispered, "Now, when you feel that you're starting to come, as it's beginning, as the feeling starts to overwhelm you, take that energy, that intensity, and move it where my fingers are showing you, move it up your spine, and I will guide you with my hand." I breathed deeply, stayed locked in his eyes, and willed the sensations, the incredibly powerful feelings, where his fingers were guiding them.

Almost hypnotically, I began to feel it move, to suddenly soar toward his fingers, up my spine, and up into the top of my head, exploding in a rush of fireworks with an intensity I had never felt before.

My body was literally engulfed with pleasure, amazement and wonderment at the incredible level of experience. All the while, I was locked into his eyes with an intensity so profound that it made time stand still.

When the feelings finally began to subside, he looked at me with a smile of such sweetness and understanding, knowing we had surpassed anything we had ever known of each other.

And in the aftermath of an overwhelming sense of wonderment, he whispered gently that this was only the beginning of our journey into the exquisitely beautiful world of Tantra.

And so, dear ones, I reluctantly leave you with the wish for you to be able to experience Tantra for yourselves, on whatever level you desire. I know that you can, and I also know it is an experience you deserve.

CHAPTER 50

THE BEST IS YET TO COME

W hen I first heard the phrase, "You're not getting older, you're getting better," I remember thinking what a lovely way of putting it, but I wonder if it's true. Well, now that I am older, I can, with extreme pleasure, assure you that it is most definitely true, although I had no idea it was going to be this way. To be quite honest, it comes as a delightful surprise.

Looking back, I remember having a tremendous lack of self-confidence when I was first discovering my own sexuality. It wasn't that the idea of sex didn't send shivers of excitement and anticipation down my spine. On the contrary, my heart practically jumped out of my chest at the mere thought of it. It was just that I was as far from being the sultry sophisticate as a human being could be without actually leaving the planet.

  In a way, it's sort of like driving a car. It takes a bit of time behind the wheel before you can start to enjoy the ride. Imagine my delight when I discovered how much more satisfying the ride can become. It may sound strange, but now that my daughter is grown and no longer a child, I seem to have reached a sexual awakening. I actually think about it more, look forward to it more and thoroughly and completely enjoy it more.

I can't tell you exactly why or give you detailed scientific explanations. I can only tell you that experience can sometimes be the best teacher. And, as a woman who has experienced a great deal of life in many different ways, I've grown and matured into someone who is able to share and enjoy a loving, caring, intimate sexual relationship. And believe me, that's not something about which I can become complacent or that I take for granted. I'm happy that I'm able to continue growing. I'm also aware that growth is a never-ending process and that process allows our understanding of life to unfold with its own natural grace. How lovely to realize that the best is yet to come.

I remember sitting in a movie theater watching *Cocoon* and thoroughly enjoying the sight of Jessica Tandy jumping into Hume Cronyn's bed. And as the Baby Boomers become collectively older, I think the collective libidos not only will maintain their momentum, but will actually increase. And that increase will not be contingent upon an influx of magical power from alien forces.

I truly feel that the older one gets, the more confident, relaxed and secure one becomes with one's own sexuality. And that is when it really becomes fun.

Fun means sex without pressure, sex without expectation and sex without performance anxiety. How could sex possibly be any fun with all those negative conditions imposed upon them?

My lover and I never impose sexual report cards on each other. We're too busy enjoying the sheer pleasure we're able to share, and the older I become, the

...growth is a never-ending process...

more that pleasure seems to deepen.

Sometimes I see older couples in their Golden Years who seem to have the most beautiful, relaxed intimacy with each other. But it also seems they have this twinkle in their eyes when they look at each other. I'm finally beginning to get a good idea of what that twinkle is all about. The glow that emanates from these couples is born of shared experiences, shared pleasures and keeping their sexual relationship alive and well.

People are living longer and staying healthier than ever before. From my perspective, men like Sean Connery, Paul Newman, Clint Eastwood, Harry Belafonte, Sidney Poitier, Quincy Jones, Warren Beatty and Al Pacino, just to name a few, are all smolderingly sexual and hotter than ever.

Equally high on the smoldering scale are the exquisitely beautiful Catherine Deneuve, Jane Fonda, Susan Sarandon, Cher, Joan Collins, Diahann Carroll, Bernadette Peters, Sophia Loren, Beverly Johnson and Lauren Hutton. And no list of agelessly beautiful women would be complete without the addition of Eartha Kitt and Lena Horne.

The self-assurance and sensuality within all of these people is beautifully and effortlessly intertwined and exudes an irresistible and unmistakable magnetic attraction.

It's funny—as I'm writing this, I just happen to recall the title of a song called "The Future's So Bright, I've Got to Wear Shades," so I hope you'll excuse me for just a moment while I look for my sunglasses.

CHAPTER 51

THE ULTIMATE
REWARD

I n this, my final chapter, I've decided to share with you
one of my favorite quotes. Pablo Picasso, when asked
about his feelings toward women, is reputed to have said,
"A woman is either a goddess or a doormat." I consider this
statement incendiary at the very least. During the numerous
times I have quoted Mr. Picasso, I've been met with
responses that range from an outraged "What a male chau-
vinist pig," to a contemplative "He's right, I totally agree."

And yet, whether Picasso was right or wrong is, to me,
almost irrelevant. What I find much more significant is the
incredible intensity and diversity of the emotional responses
precipitated by his remark. But what I feel is most significant is the importance of understanding the reasons behind
this polemic and the overwhelming effect of those responses
upon relationships between men and women.

Unfortunately for many men, there is a comfort zone in
which acceptance of a black-and-white stereotypical assess-
ment of women is consistently reinforced as the status quo.
Equally unfortunate is the fact that far too many women
unwittingly or subconsciously also perceive themselves at one
extreme or the other, sometimes vacillating between the two.

And while we're on the subject of the extreme and absurd, the cliché that a man is either macho or a wimp has also caused men to feel much more conflict and insecurity than they care to admit, even to themselves.

To me, the perpetuation of either of these ridiculous and divisive attitudes is hardly conducive to making a smooth transition from the battlefield to the boudoir. And yet—considering the enormous vulnerability and complexity of the human heart and mind—walking on water would seem to be more easily accomplished than ending the battle of the sexes; a battle that, unfortunately, continues predominately because of mutual distrust. For example, when a woman is perceived in the oversimplified extreme of either goddess or doormat, she becomes much easier for a man to "figure out." She ceases to be the covert threat that persistently puzzles, frustrates and perplexes him. The unpredictable and unfathomable nature of woman engenders an ambivalence so great that a man will, on the one hand, do everything he can to subjugate, denigrate and devalue her; while on the other hand, with equal fervor, he idolizes, adores and worships the ground upon which she walks. Women, however, honestly feel that they are able to perceive men much more realistically, and if their initial expectations of a man exceed his capabilities, they are more willing to be malleable in order to "make the relationship work."

...without communication, men and women have nothing between them...

But if they begin to feel as though they're bending into a pretzel in order to be accommodating, the monster of resentment begins to rear its ugly head. And when that resentment inevitably takes over, the couple will quickly find themselves in "relationship hell."

Now if "relationship hell" sounds all too

familiar, you are definitely not alone. In fact, it's usually standing room only because, unfortunately, we all know exactly where that place is located. And to add insult to injury, we've all spent far more time there than we ever could possibly have imagined in our worst nightmares. Unfortunately, the only comfort we've had while residing there is in looking around and seeing most of our friends.

Predictably, the main topic of conversation was usually not how or why we got there but how miserable we were to be there, especially since it was certainly not our fault and that, of course, we were definitely leaving there at any moment—as soon as we found the exit sign. And that dishonestly confident remark was usually quickly followed by the thinly disguised panic-stricken questions: "You don't happen to know the way out of here, do you? You don't? What do you mean you don't think there is one?"

Well, after having spent more than enough time in "relationship hell"—but fortunately learning a great deal while I was there—I can assure you that not only is there definitely a way out, but there is also a way to assure yourself of never having to return.

And the way to accomplish the seemingly impossible—the way to bridge the ever-widening gap between men and women, the way to take that first step to begin to understand each other—is to implement my Eleventh Erotic Commandment: the commandment of communication. Because without communication, men and women have nothing between them but a brick wall, and I guarantee you, every brick in that wall is a misunderstanding. Every time you and your lover are willing to be honest with each other and share your true feelings, however, no matter how difficult or painful or risky that may be, you take away a certain number of bricks. Finally, when enough bricks are taken away, you and your lover will be able to see each other clearly, perhaps for the first time. And that experience will be both frightening and exhilarating, simply because it's so new. You will also begin to feel the magic of a new awareness of each other. An awareness for which you've both worked quite hard.

The next step is that you will actually begin to understand each other's feelings, responses and behavior, to the degree that your acceptance of each other ultimately becomes truly effortless. Your knowledge of each other will begin to unfold naturally, with its own momentum, its own ease. If you implement all my erotic commandments, the discovery of each other and the closeness and intimacy engendered by that discovery will be its own reward.

And despite the overt and quite obvious differences between men and women, I still find it wonderful that we are able to laugh together in the same way about the same things which give us pleasure, cry in the same way about the things which cause us sorrow, hurt in the same way about the things which cause us pain.

Externally, we may manifest these feelings differently, but deep within the core of our beings, our emotions as men and women are absolutely the same.

And yet, there can never be a complacency about the qualities that we have in common, because in the next second, we can be completely engulfed by the magnitude of our differences.

How does one explain the incredible magnetic attraction and repulsion between us, the ineffable polarity, the hypnotic yin and yang, the overwhelming degree of love and hate we inspire in each other, the extent to which we cause each other to be sexually and emotionally swept away? From the beginning of recorded time, humankind has been trying to unravel these mysteries—but to no avail.

The great thing is that despite the fact that no one seems to be able to figure out or even begin to understand the powerful attraction between the sexes, and all the ridiculous problems that attraction continues to cause, it has never stopped men and women from their relentless pursuit of each other.

That pursuit is beautifully celebrated in every form of art, music, dance, literature and cinema. It is celebrated in every part of the world, in every language, every race, every nationality. The expressions of love are timeless and the language of love is universal. It is the language of which no one ever tires or seems to get enough!

In Shakespeare's *Romeo and Juliet*, Juliet, in conveying her love for Romeo, whispers, "My bounty is boundless as the sea, my love as deep; the more I give to thee, the more I have, for both are infinite."

The more giving you and your lover are to each other, the more you will each have to give, the more you share with each other, the more there will be to share, and the more pleasure and enjoyment you give to each other, the more pleasure and enjoyment you will receive. This is one of life's most wonderful phenomena, one of life's greatest and most powerful mysteries, and one that doesn't really need to be solved, but simply appreciated.

To strive for this knowledge of each other on whatever levels you are able to share—whether they are emotional, mental, physical, sexual or spiritual—is to begin to understand that they are all interrelated and intertwined. And when these levels within the two of you begin to magically coalesce, with it will come the discovery of the most incredible mutual awareness, communication and understanding. This is what being a world-class lover really means: to thrill in the pleasure of being with each other and the pleasure you are able to give to and receive from each other.

This is what women want, and this is what men really want—both with each other and for themselves. And I promise you, in achieving this goal, you will experience all the mystery, the passion, the joy and the fulfillment of genuine intimacy; intimacy that has been earned—intimacy that is real. This kind of intimacy is truly the ultimate reward.